THE ODIC FORCE

LETTERS ON OD AND MAGNETISM

By

KARL VON REICHENBACH

Translations and Introduction by

F. D. O'Byrne

Published 2000
The Book Tree
Escondido, CA

First published by Hutchinson & Co., London, 1926.

Printed on Acid-Free Paper

The Odic Force
ISBN 1-58509-001-8

©2000
THE BOOK TREE
All Rights Reserved

FOREWARD

What is the odic force? This is a vital energy or life force that permeates all living plants, animals, and humans. It has gone by a number of different names in different cultures around the world—called *prana* in India, *mana* in Hawaii, Mesmer called it *animal magnetism*, Gallien called it *pneuma*, Fludd called it *spiritus*, it was *astral light* to the Kaballists, and the ancient sage Hermes Trismegistus referred to it as *telesma*. All this came before Dr. von Reichenbach, a German, stumbled across this power and decided to do some experiments to actually prove that it exists. The experiments revealed that *od*, as he called it, truly does exist and could well be the most important force in the universe.

Von Reichenbach published his findings in 1845 in the form of this book. It was ridiculed by his peers and established scientists despite the fact that he was an expert on meteorites and had a brilliant background as a chemist and a metallurgist. Yet no one gave any validation or credit to his findings in any major way.

Von Reichenbach was the first person to approach this force scientifically, having conducted hundreds of careful experiments. But the scientific community ignored his findings because they had just finished debunking Mesmer's *animal magnetism* (the same force with a different name) and were not willing to listen to anything else along similar lines, regardless of its accompanying proof. It's amazing that most fellow scientists were willing to dismiss von Reichenbach without reviewing the evidence. One of them went so far as to interfere with his public experiments and attempt to upset and antagonize those witnessing the work.

At this time science had just replaced religion, for the most part, as the most trusted authority on all matters of importance. The universe was being broken down and examined in a verifiable and scientific manner. It was materialism vs. spiritualism, and if any scientist dared to explore anything that was slightly spiritual, they became a laughingstock. When von Reichenbach found this strange force that crossed into the realm of being spiritual, or having some sort of spiritual element, it did not deter his scientific mind.

He began to work with people who were sensitive enough to accurately detect the polarity of magnets because they could *see* it. These people could also see the human aura—an energy field connected to the human body, plus detect an energy-related color spectrum that was directly linked to metals and minerals. They could either feel or taste the odic force in various substances and liquids, plus determine the polarity of this force and exactly when it had a positive or negative effect upon people.

Many of these findings were later backed up by a brilliant man in the twentieth century named Wilhelm Reich. Reich, like von Reichenbach, claimed that this force could be detected visually and thermetically in plants, animals, and in the atmosphere. They both agreed that its color was blue. When Reich rediscovered this force he called it *orgone energy*. He developed what he called an "orgone accumulator," meant to gather this energy for the benefit of its recipient and it was designed for therapeutic purposes. The FDA tested it and announced it as being worthless, but the "experts" who tested the device and made the announcement remained anonymous. Reich was ordered to stop making and selling orgone accumulators and was given a gag order to not mention the word "orgone" in any of his books. Reich refused, and continued his work. He was eventually arrested, fined, and jailed.

He had come to the United States, the land of the free, to avoid this kind of treatment after his work had been either banned or burned in Nazi Germany and in Communist Russia. But on August 23, 1956, U.S. authorities burned Reich's books to suppress his information. On November 3, 1957, Wilhelm Reich died in prison at the age of 60.

Von Reichenbach, a century earlier, was never imprisoned but he did spend his later years dissillusioned as to why his work was never accepted. Later, in 1883, an investigative committee was formed by the Society for Psychical Research in London, and they were able to validate many of von Reichenbach's original claims.

Considering the treatment of Wilhelm Reich, who followed on von Reichenbach's heels, it is highly suspected that those who would take up this work even today would experience opposition, suppression, and persecution. The real reasons behind such suppression can only be speculated upon, but one thing is clear—the "powers that be" do not want this subject breached or studied to any significant degree. People are amazed to learn that the U.S. government, just a few short decades ago, engaged itself in book burning, suppressing information, and jailing a brilliant scientist to the point of causing his death. It is time to start asking why, and to investigate the subject further.

Von Reichenbach wrote this book as a simplified version of a more advanced text, making the work easy to study for those who wish to grasp the subject. With this book, there is no better place to start. It is our hope that such material, and a more complete understanding of it, can move humanity's understanding of itself and the universe forward.

Paul Tice

ANALYTICAL TABLE OF CONTENTS

Introduction :

v

CONTENTS

CONTENTS

INTRODUCTION

WHY should a scientist of eminence be denied a hearing for observations of fact to which he has devoted a quarter of a century of the best years of his life?

Fact, they say, is like steam; deny it an exit, and you are bound sooner or later to have an explosion. How much more dignified to take fact quietly!

A society for the conservation and recovery of scientific observations might, I have often thought, do immense service to humanity: what has been lost, destroyed, or suppressed in the realm of knowledge bears so large a proportion to the amount that enters actually into our tradition! Atlantis has passed away, and so has the twice-wrecked library of Alexandria; but of the truth suppressed by the blindness of officialdom there is many a brand that may yet be plucked from the burning. Salvage may still be effected. Let it be so in Reichenbach's case.

In every age some truth discovered is lost because it is unwelcome truth—not unwelcome, perhaps, so much to the mass of mankind directly, as unwelcome to certain official custodians of learning, in whom an overworked, or indolent, or, it may be, cowardly humanity reposes a childlike, and often quite unjustified, confidence. Men find the path of belief so much easier to tread than the arduous path of learning, and thus they come to entrust their interests to lawyers and politicians, scientists and priests. Is it any wonder if they are robbed of truth wholesale? It is the penalty they bear for non-compliance with

ix

nature's wholesome law that " every man shall bear his own burden." They should think, and find out, and know for themselves.

Thus many an important truth is lost to humanity simply because it has once proved unwelcome to officialdom. The comfortably placed official, knowing that he knows more than most men, is apt to let his mental position of solidity degenerate into one of stolidity. He grows gradually averse from any idea of change whatsoever, of any change, above all, that would make him alter his general outlook upon life. He clings to his *Weltanschauung* as he does to his own soul—or salary.

In his caricature of conservatism the degenerate official is the antithesis of the artist, as he is of the true scientist. Your artist is your great empiric, and so is your scientist. Both work their way to their respective ends by constant shift and change. The very breath of art is the trial of a thousand forms under the influence of a thousand imaginings until the perfection of form results. The scientist, too, forms and reforms, experiments and re-experiments, under all imaginably pertinent conditions, and gives every possibility its chance, in his chase of that charmingly beautiful, but elusive. nymph, Truth.

It is quite otherwise, however, with a representative of science who, being all too average a man, is official first and experimentalist afterwards. Merely having to make room for a new theory in the laboriously and expensively erected government-buildings of science causes him a feeling of discomfort, and the prospect of discomfort arouses within him, as Reichenbach notes in his Preface, the spirit of opposition. Why upset everything ? he asks : there are no two

branches of science disconnected.   What a bore!
Now the whole house that Jack built will have to
be taken to pieces, replanned, and reset.   And,
moreover, he reflects, the change may turn out in
the end to have been a *needless* bore.   It may all
be a scare.   And so he sits solid, and diamagnetic—
unattracted, unattractive : reflecting for his comfort that he has at least the *vis inertiae* of the universe
on his side.   "*Gut Ding nimmt Zeit*," he says :
" Anything big needs plenty of time." So he salves
his soul.

Is the official always to be blamed for this mental
attitude ?   Perhaps not always and entirely—provided, of course, that no meaner motive, no motive
of which conscience accuses, comes in to make him
look the other way when he sees the man of forceful
imagination coming along.   Who outside the charmed
circle of officialdom may feel so sure of self as to be
the official's judge ?

But is it any wonder if thus, under the domination
of " the average man " a mass of indubitable truth,
and sometimes brilliantly discovered truth, settles
down into the dust of learned libraries ?   Or that it
remains there undisturbed for ages, while mortals
swink to discover for themselves what their brother
has discovered for their benefit ages before ?

It is not only the obscure worker who may find his
best work thus unwelcome, and thus consigned to
oblivion.   Men of the highest gifts and recognized
position in the intellectual world have fallen victims
to this particular stroke of fate.   " Fortune of war!
Fortune of war ! " as the old soldier in Louis XI's
Scottish guard philosophized in *Quentin Durward*.
Even a Socrates was silenced as a corruptor of youth,
and a Plato explained away as a writer of fairy-tales.

Berzelius was charged of senility by a brother scientist for his approval of Reichenbach's unwelcome *Researches*. Baron Justus von Liebig was denounced by another for their publication in his *Annals*, as having " brought a misery upon physical science for which there was no excuse." Even the great Goethe, scientist in the noblest sense of the word, is only beginning now, in 1925, to find recognition for his " relativity " theory of light and colour, published, in correction of the Newtonian theory of 1672, as far back as 1810.

Goethe (1749–1832) anticipated Reichenbach's observations of the luminosity of plants by about a quarter of a century, and the two independent discoverers are still awaiting, hand in hand, the general recognition of their services in this direction by the scientific world. Radiology and relativity are our latest words in science, and Goethe and Reichenbach were both radiologists and relativists—only about a century too soon.

Dr. Guenther Wachsmuth of the " Goetheanum " Institute in Basel, Switzerland, assures us in his Preface to Dr. Friedrich Graevell's reprinted work (from the 1st edition of 1857), *Goethe in the Right against Newton* (2nd ed. 1922, p. xix), that " the world of dead mechanism " set up by the school of Sir Isaac Newton has at last collapsed and vanished from the modern school of scientific thought, while " the world of living organism " pictured by Goethe in his studies on light and colour in 1810 is now the world accepted by all live men of science. Have the purely materialistic scientists, then, had their day ? Are *they* now the ghosts on earth ? And do we see the steel-worker joining hands with the poet to oust them for the benefit of our so-called " spiritualists " ? It seems a pretty little human comedy; and Dr. Graevell, M.D., who has been campaigning in Berlin for justice to Goethe since 1857, must be thoroughly enjoying it.

But it may be the sober truth. Reichenbach, metallurgist and manufacturer, certainly seems to supplement and confirm Goethe's theory of light by his highly original researches, and to supply us at the same time with **a scientific basis for the facts of the " spirit-intercourse "** now puzzling so many. To put this scientific basis at the disposal of the English-reading world, as Reichenbach's works are little more than bibliographical curiosities in Germany, is the object of the present book.

Before going further, I shall quote an anecdote of Baron Alexander von Humboldt (1769–1859) (*Membre de l'Institut de France et de l'Académie Française*, and unquestionably the most honoured physical scientist of his day), from Reichenbach's *Odic Occurrences in Berlin in the Years* 1861 *and* 1862 (p. 57), as it seems to me decidedly pertinent to my present purpose :

" In the June of 1853 Alexander von Humboldt sat at the royal table in Berlin, and General Bertrand and Lieut.-General Graf von Lüttichau were sitting next to him. I am authorized by the latter to make use of his person and name for the publication of an observation made by Von Humboldt upon this occasion. Bertrand had led the conversation on to the subject of table-turning and so on, which was a novelty at the time, and when the talk had been bandied about for a space on the subject, Humboldt closed it sententiously with the words : **'The facts are undeniable ; it now becomes the task of science to explain them.'** "

Unfortunately the historical record shows that the task he indicated was one which science—in Berlin at least—deliberately shirked, though its leading professors of physics were afforded the best possible opportunity of putting it in hand by Reichenbach himself. As the object of this Introduction to the *Odic-Magnetic Letters* is to draw attention to Reichenbach's high scientific authority, and to insist upon his obtaining a hearing as one distinguished by such, I shall detail the facts connected with this fateful encounter of his with the professors of the University of Berlin, in the years 1861–2, in the course of a short sketch of his life and scientific achievements.

To make my sketch of Reichenbach's career as objective as possible to the English reader's mind, and clear myself at the outset from all reproach of a Turnerian colouration of fact, I shall start by candidly admitting (and deploring) the absence of any notice of so eminent a scientist and discoverer in the *Encyclopædia Britannica*. Explain the omission I cannot. I must also admit the fact that there is no extant biography of Reichenbach in book form anywhere that I can discover. I am reduced to drawing the materials for my sketch of his career almost exclusively from the brief but effective notices in the *Grande Encyclopédie* and the *Allgemeine Deutsche Biographie* (published in 1888 at the instance of the King of Bavaria by the Historical Commission of the Royal Academy of Sciences), and from the German controversial literature dealing with the subject of odic force when it was first mooted. But I shall translate verbatim and in their entirety the short judgments of Reichenbach's character and work that appear in the two standard reference books mentioned, as I wish the English reader to know the plain facts, pro and con, and to let him draw his conclusions for himself.

Carl Reichenbach was born at Stuttgart, the capital of the kingdom of Württemberg, on 12th February, 1788, and died at Leipsic in Saxony on 22nd January, 1869. His life's chronology thus ran fairly parallel with that of our own great scientific discoverer, Michael Faraday, who was born at Newington Butts, London, on 22nd September, 1791, and died at Hampton Court Green on 25th August, 1867. Reichenbach thus lived nearly 81 years, and Faraday nearly 76 ; but Faraday only retained his mental faculties unimpaired till about the age of 50, whereas Reichenbach's lasted till death.

Reichenbach's father was the Court Librarian in Stuttgart, and had his son educated at the local Gymnasium or High School, and afterwards at the State University of Tübingen, where the young man followed a course of natural science, political economy, and—Poggendorff says (*Biogr.-liter. Handwörterbuch*)—law. At that time, it will be remembered, Germany was completely under the political dictatorship of France, and held, in fact, as a conquered country in the iron military grip of Napoleon I. Reichenbach's native force of character may be judged from the fact that, as a boy of sixteen years of age, he founded a secret society for setting up a German Reich in the South Sea Islands, and actually, in spite of his years, got a large number of followers ; but, in the ordinary way of secret societies, he soon found himself betrayed to the authorities in actual possession of Government authority. He was arrested by the Napoleonic police, subjected to examination, and detained for some months as a political prisoner in the fortress of Hohenasperg.

On his release, he resumed his studies, and obtained

his degree of Ph.D.—Philosophiæ Doctor—which is equivalent to graduation, whether as Bachelor of Science or Bachelor of Arts, in an English University. The German University curriculum, the English reader may perhaps like to be reminded, is commonly divided into the two great branches of theology and philosophy, both science and arts being clustered upon the latter, together with all the systems of all the philosophers, from Pythagoras of Samos down to Rudolf Eucken of Jena. Reichenbach's writings give evidence now and again of a philosophic vein of no mean calibre ; but it is a philosophy controlled by plain, healthy good-sense and the true instinct of a scientist, such as we strictly understand the scientific instinct in our own day. At any rate, it is quite plain in what a utilitarian, as well as scientific, direction his interests mainly ran at the University of Tübingen ; for we find his first publication recorded in Poggendorff's *Biographical Literary Dictionary for the History of the Exact Sciences*, under year 1811, as *Dissertatio de nova constructione follis hydrostatici*, Tübingen, evidently the original work he had, in accordance with University rule, to print and submit for examination before presentation to his doctorate— a " dissertation on a new design for constructing a hydrostatic bellows ! "

The year before that, in 1810, Goethe had published his two-volume scientific work : *Zur Farbenlehre, A Theory of Colour*, contravening, or perhaps better said more fully extending, correcting from the " relativity " standpoint, and bringing from a maimed condition into a perfect, symmetrical whole the optical theory advanced by Sir Isaac Newton in 1672, just one hundred and thirty-eight years before. We can easily, from subsequent history, imagine what its effect must have been on the young

Carl Reichenbach's mind, and how it may have drawn his attention at an early stage to the relativity of light and its presence in what had hitherto been plumply regarded as darkness.

On concluding his University studies, Dr. Reichenbach travelled over France and Germany investigating the construction and commercial exploitation of ironworks, and ended in 1815 by setting up a works for himself at Villingen in the Duchy of Baden. Later on he built the first great charcoal furnaces at Hausach, also in Baden. In 1821 he got into touch with Count Hugo zu Salm in Vienna, in partnership with whom he established a group of metallurgical and allied works at Blansko in Moravia, where he also signalized himself by erecting and organizing the complicated business of a beet-sugar factory, which enriched both the town of Blansko and himself, and at the same time brought the name of Reichenbach into high repute throughout Central Europe. Reichenbach's wealth increased rapidly : he bought the landed estates of Gutenbrunn and Neidlung in Lower Austria, Nisco in Galicia, and Reisenberg near Vienna, to which he added the steelworks of Ternitz (Lower Austria) and the blast-furnaces of Gaya (Moravia). Taking into the account the metallurgical establishments already owned by him in the Duchy of Baden, he may be said to have held sway like a sort of industrial prince from the Danube to the Rhine.

The year 1825 was marked in the world of applied science by Faraday's discovery of benzole, the basis of our modern aniline colour dyes. On 16th June last we celebrated the centenary of the event at the same Royal Institution at which Faraday first announced the discovery by his paper, " On New Compounds of Carbon and Hydrogen," and among the useful things said at the centenary celebration a leash of strictures let loose on scientists and men of letters simultaneously by Professor N. E. Armstrong seems to deserve commemoration. He complained (1) " that men of letters paid no heed to discovery, and that the public had no knowledge of it ; and (2) that science to-day was too prone to speculate, and differed from Faraday with his love for the children's lectures in its entirely selfish use of jargon."—*The Times*, 17th June, 1925. This bears on Reichenbach's present book.

There is unfortunately an idea prevalent to-day that writings conveying exact knowledge in an easily memorizable form do not, however eloquent or perfect their expression, constitute literature properly so called. Literature, it seems to be assumed, must be either fiction, poetry, or writing in which fancy and imagination play the principal part—a groundless assumption, probably based on the widespread habit of kill-time novel-reading. The prevalence of such a state of opinion among the paying patrons of literature, favouring fancy, speculation, and idealistic comment rather than the exposition of fact, may go far to account for " men of letters paying no heed to discovery."

Then, again, scientific speculation based largely on calculations in the higher mathematics, and expounded chiefly for the benefit of the few who are sufficient masters of a technical " jargon," certainly tends, as Professor Armstrong points out, to leave most men's mentality just as it was before the event of actual scientific discovery. The professor's protest may well serve as a text for drawing attention to Reichenbach's admirably genial style in conveying scientific knowledge in popular language, and that, too, on so recondite a subject as the discovery announced in the *Odic-Magnetic Letters*, which are based on a series of laborious experiments running into thousands, and involving the observation of many hundreds of human subjects of all classes, conditions, and characters. The result is that his *Odic-Magnetic Letters*, in spite of the concentrated nature of the information they contain, are calculated to impart far more " thrills " to the ordinarily intelligent reader than many a popular novel of equal bulk. In this respect of didactic power Reichenbach quite parallels the naïve expository genius of Faraday. And both Faraday and Reichenbach were experimentalists first, and speculators long, long afterwards.

In point of utility, Reichenbach rivalled Faraday's discovery of benzole just five years later by his discovery of paraffin, in 1830, in the same department of hydrocarbons. Faraday had turned his attention meanwhile to light and optics, but Reichenbach held on at his coal-tar products and discovered in 1831 eupion (Greek: *eu*, very ; *pion*, greasy), a limpid and highly volatile inflammable liquid obtained by destructive distillation of vegetable substances, in 1832 creosote (Greek: *kreos*, flesh, meat ; *soter*, preserver), the well-known antiseptic fluid, turned to such extensive account ever since for the preservation of submarine piles, railway sleepers, etc., from wet rot and dry rot, and in 1833 pittacal (Greek: *pitta*, pitch, tar ; *kalos*, beautiful), the beautiful dark-blue, solid substance resembling indigo found in wood-tar, now used in dyeing, and which, I suppose, has done its share in putting down the market value of the genuine indigo from India, obtained by infusion from the anil plant. Reichenbach laid much stress from the outset on the therapeutic value of creosote : he was always greatly interested in hygiene and therapy.

Meanwhile, Faraday, whose movements Reichenbach may be presumed to have followed pretty closely, had reported to the Royal Society (1829) on the " Manufacture of Glass for Optical Purposes "—which has since fallen almost entirely into German hands—and had manufactured his own famous " heavy glass," not much use in optics, but destined to be turned to splendid account in his glow studies on what he called " lines of electric force " in 1845. He had read in 1831, the eupion year, his paper " On a Peculiar Class of Optical Deceptions," to which the chromatrope owes its origin—which has a close bearing on Goethe's work—and had then turned his attention to experiments in the domain of magneto-electricity, discovering before very long that electricity is " induced " by moments of magnetization and demagnetization.

I beg my reader not to consider these references to Faraday's work purely otiose—his work and Reichenbach's explain each other mutually : and a reference to Letter xiv. on the Odic Spectrum and Polarity of the Earth, giving Reichenbach's electro-magnetic sphere experiments, will bear me out in this statement. The two great men are to be studied together throughout their career, and the student will find that they illustrate and—what is still better—explain each other at innumerable points, even at the single point, that of the " table-turning " phenomenon, where at first sight, but only at first sight, they seem for a moment to come into violent collision. This will be made clear before the close of my Introduction.

Pursuing his electrical experiments, Faraday, on 23rd May, 1833, read his paper before the Royal Society on a " New Law of Electric Conduction," namely, the influence of the state of aggregation on electrical conductors, the self-same substance conducting or refusing to conduct according as it is liquid or solid—e.g. water and ice (see Letters ix. and xii.). This was followed up by the paper of 10th and 17th June, 1833, " On the Identity of Electricities," namely, those of the pile or battery, the machine, the gymnotus and torpedo, and magneto—and thermo-electricity. During the years following, up to 1841, when Faraday's health broke down, he paid considerable attention to electrical and chemical problems, seeking to define the differences between these two forces. He proved by his " voltameter " that the decompositions of the voltaic battery are as definite in their character as the chemical combinations which gave birth to the atomic theory, and proved, furthermore, that the true source of voltaic power consists in chemical action, and not in mere contact of the different metals—otherwise a perpetual effect (and perpetual motion) would have been postulated. In connection with these results arrived at by Faraday, Reichenbach's tables of " Differences " between od and the three forces of heat, electricity, and magnetism claim attention. I shall condense them from his *Researches* (see Gregory's edition of 1850, pp. 228–42 for the full text), and insert them in their proper place later on as a supplement. They will show that Reichenbach kept pretty closely in touch with Faraday's work as just noted.

Meantime, Reichenbach's business partner, Count Hugo zu Salm, had died, and Reichenbach had been so tormented by the Count's sons, who alleged mismanagement and irregularities in his conduct of the business, that he was forced to take a legal action against them for slander. In this action, so particularly distracting and obnoxious to a man of scientific temper and occupations, he was entirely successful. The case was heard in 1836, and in 1839 Reichenbach was created Baron, or *Freiherr*, von Reichenbach by the King of Württemberg. He seems to have withdrawn his attention largely from business affairs after that date, and to have devoted himself, at his Castle of Reisenberg, to the scientific *Researches* which have since made his name so famous, and are epitomized for the general reader in the present volume of *Odic-Magnetic Letters*.

Reichenbach first published the results of his observations in a series of seven papers entitled " Researches on Magnetism, Electricity, Heat, and Light in their relations to Vital Power," which appeared in March and May, 1845 as a special supplement to Liebig and Wöhler's famous *Annals of Chemistry* : they had been submitted to the editors' consideration in June–July, 1844. A few years later an English edition of the *Annals* was published regularly by Taylor, Walton, and Maberly, the scientific book-dealers of 28 Upper Gower Street, W.C. ; but their series only started with the year 1847 ; so that the *Researches* were not in the way of engaging the attention of the English-speaking scientific world.

Under the circumstances, Dr. William Gregory, M.D., a chemical scientist of high distinction, who had just been appointed Professor of Chemistry (1844) at the University of Edinburgh, and who had, moreover, been a favourite pupil of Baron von Liebig's at Giessen, was authorized by Reichenbach to translate the *Researches* into English. Gregory first published an *Abstract* of them in English early in 1846. This *Abstract* condensed all essential matter, he tells us, into about one-half the bulk of the original.

It was a great success. " Not only was the edition

very rapidly sold," wrote Gregory in 1850 (Preface to the *Researches*, p. ix), " but I have been ever since 1846 favoured with letters of enquiry concerning a new edition, and of high approval of the work, so numerous, that I have found it quite impossible to return answers individually to nearly the whole of them." He adds that the *Abstract* " was favourably noticed in various scientific and literary journals, as well as in the daily press. Indeed, up to this time [1850]," he continues, " I have not become acquainted with any scientific criticisms published in this country on the Author's researches, which require any notice from me in this place. This, as will be seen by the Author's Preface, forms a strong and favourable contrast with the reception given to Part I by various men of science in Germany. . . . It must be gratifying to the numerous English readers of the *Abstract* to know—and to this I can myself testify—that the lamented Berzelius took a very deep interest in the investigation, and expressed in a letter to the editor (i.e. Gregory himself) that it could not possibly have been in better hands than those of Baron von Reichenbach."

The Part I of the *Researches* referred to comprised the seven papers published by Baron Liebig in his *Annalen der Chemie* in 1845. Reichenbach continued a laborious and minute study of all branches of the subject, but in particular of the luminous phenomena of magnets as seen by the sensitive, and the results he published in 1849–50 were almost entirely concerned with magnets. They were added to the *Researches* as Part II, and both parts were published in Brunswick in book form, 2 volumes, entitled : *Untersuchungen über die Dynamide des Magnetismus, der Elektrizität, der Wärme, des Lichtes, in ihren Beziehungen zur Lebenskraft—Researches into the*

Forces of Magnetism, Electricity, Heat, and Light, in relation to the Force of Life. Gregory put the new complete work in hand without delay, and brought out his English edition in 1850 in one large 8vo volume of xlv., 463 pages, with three sheets of illustrative plates, the first portion of the work receiving the additional title of : " Physico-physiological Researches on the Imponderables in their relation to Vital Force ; Part I, Second Edition corrected and improved."

When Reichenbach began his studies of abnormal sense-power, he seems at first to have thought that it was only to be looked for among persons in ill-health, cataleptic patients, and so on, and only discovered later that it existed, and even to a far greater degree, among persons in good health. This explains why the experiments in Part I of his *Researches* were conducted mostly with sick persons, and only with a few who were healthy, while in Part II the sensitives chosen for experimentation were, with very few exceptions, taken from the ranks of the healthy. A list of 61 of these persons of abnormal psychic powers living in Vienna, with exact addresses added in the case of a few of the obscurer among them, is given for reference ; the names cover all classes of society, from the highest to the lowest, and include those of many scientists ; 31 are female in sex, and 30 male. Among the scientist sensitives, 6 were holders of high offices, while 7 of the total 13 were undistinguished by high office, but obviously persons of the highest education. Of the nobility and gentry, titled ladies numbered 4, and titled gentlemen 2—Baron August von Oberlaender, of Schebetau, Moravia, and Chevalier Hubert von Rainer of Klagenfurth. The ladies of rank and title were : (1) Baroness Maria von Augustin, (2) Miss

Wilhelmine von Weigelsberg, (3) Mrs. Hofrat von Varady, (4) Baroness Pauline von Natorp, (5) Baroness Isabella von Tessedik, (6) Baroness Elise von Seckendorf (Sondershausen, Saxony), and (7) Mrs. Von Peichich-Zimanyi.

As to the trustworthiness of the evidence obtained from the sensitives he examined, Reichenbach observes (*Researches*, ed. Gregory, p. xliii.) :

" I have not found the difficulty of getting at the truth in such investigations by any means so great and insuperable as those who dread the labour of research into the subject constantly assert it to be. . . . I must here say to the honour of the mixed population of Vienna that, among about a hundred persons whom I have examined hitherto in the course of these researches to a greater or less extent . . . hardly one was found who gave me two or three somewhat highly coloured answers ; and this, when it did occur, arose certainly more from ignorance than from any dishonest intention. Such answers were, moreover, instantly detected and rebuked by me. Considering the intrinsic natural connection in which all these phenomena stand to each other, and the threads of which connection I now firmly hold, it is absolutely impossible for anyone to deceive me, even for a few minutes, by false answers, which I should instantly discover to be false, were they attempted."

He reverted to this subject later in his *Odische Erwiderungen—Odic Rejoinders*, published in 1856, after the experience of countless further experiments, and I quote from a passage there for the convenience of the reader, while his mind is directed to this particular point (*loc. cit.*, pp. 95–6) : it was written in reply to the criticisms of Gustav Theodor Fechner, a religious-minded man and a professional scientist (Professor of Physics in the University of Leipsic), but a scientist mortally afraid of seeing ghosts (see his famous *Life After Death*, 1835, Wernekke's trans., 1906, pp. 103–5) :

"Oh no," rejoins Reichenbach, "they don't see it at all ; they are in an excited state of mind ; I have put them into a state of tension ; they are in a condition of ecstasy, and imagine, like Father Amis, that they perceive or see something, whereas there is nothing to be seen anywhere ; they repeat blindly whatever I suggest, and, when I suggest nothing, they repeat nevertheless what I have never said ! Come, come, is it not, too, too hasty, to attribute stupidities of this sort to me ? Is not Dr. Fechner ashamed to credit me on the one hand with all sorts of brilliant mental qualities, and on the other to treat me like a simple-minded youth ? . . . Does he quite forget the fact that at least a hundred of my two hundred sensitives are men of scientific education, and that among these there are something like fifty who are physicians, or physicists, or chemists, or mathematicians, or philosophers, men, in short, who in many cases are just on the same high level of scientific attainment as Mr. Fechner himself ? Do not these men possess a critical faculty, just as he does ? Does he not see that every basic experiment has been repeated ten, twenty, a hundred times ? Is he not satisfied with the fact that in *The Sensitive* (pp. 8–11, 15, 16) the first fundamental experiments were made with 61, then with 50, with 28, with 84, and in some cases with more than 100 repetitions, with almost innumerable changes of conditions carefully selected to bear upon the point, and made with subjects of the most varying characteristics at different intervals of time covering a period of more than 10 years?

" The number of the sensitives whom I have experimented with up to the present (1856) writing is just 197 ; I have examined at least 100 others without taking written notes ; the basic experiments consequently were carried out with nearly 300 subjects, with inexhaustible patience and in uninterrupted sequence, and yet it is not enough for Mr. Fechner that all these three hundred have unanimously—in a sort of unprecedented delirium, I suppose—experienced, seen, deposed, and confirmed one and the same thing for the space of 10 years ! If the maintenance of such an opinion, under such circumstances, is not a *reductio ad absurdum* and self-destructive, then there is no such thing as logic, and no such thing as a sound human understanding any longer in existence.

" He quite passes over the fact that I myself have been able to observe a considerable number of odic and sensitivist occurrences, not in their direct appeal to the senses, but with absolute certainty in their necessary effects and material consequences. Why does he pass them over ? Intentionally ? No, not at all ; he is far too honourable a man for that ; the reason is that he has not come across them where they are to be found, mostly in the second volume of my book, which he has not read ! " (*Fechner admits in his work, " Professor Schleiden und der Mond," 1856, p. 277, that he has only studied the first part of Reichenbach's " Researches," and that not completely, and that he has only just turned over a few of the pages in the second.*)

The hostile criticism of Reichenbach's *Researches* in Germany and Austria proceeded almost entirely, so far as I have been able to ascertain, from men who, like Fechner, would not take the trouble to seriously test his alleged results by experiments conducted by themselves. Such experiments, to be effective, would certainly require an ample fund of patience and self-sacrificing care ; but patience and self-sacrifice are good qualities to be expected of the German scientist ; in fact it is the fashion over here to assign the German almost a monopoly of these scientific virtues—in my judgment a very mistaken notion, like many others in the British tradition.

Reichenbach quotes the names of three German scientists (*Odische Erwiderungen*, p. 84 *sq.* Dr. Büchner of Tübingen, Dr. Buchmann of Alvensleben, and Dr. Neumann of Berlin, as having had the patience to make a sufficient number of the experiments and as having thereby fully confirmed his own results, and adds that there were many others besides Dr. Gregory of Edinburgh whom he could mention also as having done so. But none of these German gentlemen were, he added, among those who " laid claim to the office of high-priests of science," and it was exactly the latter class that he wished to get upon his side. He took steps to do this in January, 1861, after the ground had seemingly been sufficiently prepared by the publication of his popular summary *Odic-Magnetic Letters* (Cotta, Stuttgart, 1852, reprint 1854, 2nd ed. 1856), *The Sensitive Man and his relation to Od,* (Cotta, Stuttgart, 1858), a large, formally scientific work in 2 vols., and *The World of Plants in its relation to Sensitivity* (Vienna, Braumüller, 1858). He details all the incidents connected with this effort in a minor work of 92 pages, entitled, *Odic Events in Berlin in the Years 1861 and 1862—Odische Begebenheiten zu Berlin in den Jahren* 1861 *und* 1862 (*von K. Freiherrn von Reichenbach, Phil. Dr. & a.l. Mr., Berlin, Verlag von E. H. Schroeder, Hermann Kaiser, Unter den Linden No.* 41, 1862).

In 1861 Reichenbach was a man of the most brilliant reputation as scientist and industrialist, wherever the German language was spoken throughout the world. Moreover, he appeared before the scientific tribunal of Berlin backed by the authority and express patronage of two of the most world-renowned scientists of his day : Jöns Jacob Berzelius of Sweden, chemist and mineralogist, to whom we owe the discovery of the electro-chemical seriation of elementary substances (in correspondence with the atomic weight series established by John Dalton of Manchester), and Baron Justus von Liebig, who may be regarded as the father of modern scientific hygiene and agriculture. Furthermore, he could quote indirectly in his own favour the results coming to light from no less a scientist than the great Michael Faraday, and had not failed to do so in his *Researches* (Liebig's *Annalen*, 1845—Brunswick, 2 vols., 1850) as follows :

" I must once more refer to the term odyle (*in the 'Odic-magnetic Letters' simply called 'od'*). It will be seen that the idea expressed by it . . . very probably includes that which, a year later than I, Dr. Faraday introduced to the scientific world as a new force under the name of diamagnetism. Doubtless the British philosopher was not acquainted with my researches, although they appeared in an English dress in London (*Gregory's 'Abstract of Reichenbach's Researches,'* 1846), otherwise he would probably not have passed them over in silence, or ignored their existence.

[*Professor Tyndall, in his short Life of Faraday (Dict. of Natl. Biogr.), may be quoted to explain this : ' In* 1841 *his (Faraday's) health broke down, and for three years he did nothing, not even reading on science. . . . As soon as his health permitted, he resumed his work, and in November* 1845 *announced a discovery which he called the magnetization of light and the illumination of the lines of electric force. . . . Faraday's next great step was the discovery of diamagnetism.' . . . Reichenbach's ' Researches ' were first published in Liebig and Wöhler's ' Annalen der Chemie ' in March and May* 1845, *though they had been sent in by the author in time for their publication to have commenced in July,* 1844.

By diamagnetism (Gr. : dia, across) *is understood the repulsion of certain substances by both poles of a magnet when such substances are freely suspended between them, the effect being that the suspended substances assume a latitudinal or ' equatorial ' direction, that is, a direction at right angles to their own ' axial line,' or axis of greatest length. Such diamagnetic substances constitute by far the greater number of the* 92 *(more or less) elementary substances known to chemists, and include—it may be mentioned, for sake of example—bismuth, antimony, cadmium, gold, lead, copper, tin, zinc, mercury ; most composite substances, whether solid, liquid, or gaseous, are also diamagnetic.*

By paramagnetism (Gr. : para, beside) *is understood the action of the magnetic poles on certain substances when freely suspended between them, the effect of which is that the substances assume a longitudinal direction, that is, a direction pointing from one pole to the other with their longer axis or axial line. The paramagnetic substances are relatively few, and are iron, nickel, cobalt, palladium, titanium, and a few others.*]

" I have condensed in the term odyle the ultimate cause of all the phenomena described by me, in so far, namely, as they are not reconcilable with our previous knowledge of the essence of magnetism and the other imponderables, and in particular are transferable from the magnet to what are called unmagnetic bodies, such as metals, glass, silk, water, salts, in short all bodies. Diamagnetism was indeed recognized and made known between 1820 and 1830 by Seebeck, Munke, Büchner and Becquerel, which was also not known to Dr. Faraday. In my researches I did not meet with the fact that unmagnetic bodies place themselves when suspended across the magnetic current, and there remains between my observations and those of Dr. Faraday a chasm for the present not filled up. Yet it seems to me not impossible that we may be, as I may say, drawing the same vehicle, but by different traces. If I do not deceive myself, Dr. Faraday has laid hold of *one* of the numerous odylic threads, a singularly promising one, and with the force of his fertile genius he will promote the discovery of truth in this department. This can only redound to the advantage of science. Whether magnetism, diamagnetism, and odyle may one day be reduced to a common origin, or whether they will continue to be separated by essential differences—these are questions the solution of which appears to me to be distant. But at all events these influences include entirely new properties, both of dead and living matter, and are, on account of their universality and their all-embracing diffusion through the universe, of the highest physical importance." (Gregory's translation, London, 1850, p. 228 *sq.*).

Reichenbach seems to have taken his first steps towards securing the approbation of " the high-priests of science " in Berlin with discretion and judgment. His patronage by Baron Justus von Liebig had been resented by his critics in the Prussian capital : he writes (*Odic Events*, p. 52) : " One of them assured me that Liebig had brought a misery (*Unheil*) upon physical science for which there was no excuse, by first introducing od through the medium of his chemical journal into the scientific world, from which it could now only be banished at the expense of much time and trouble." Like Reichenbach himself, Liebig was a South German, born in Darmstadt, and Professor of Chemistry at the University of Munich. I suspect that it was not without regard to local sympathies and antipathies that Reichenbach now made his advances through Poggendorff, a native of Hamburg (1796–1877), at the time Extraordinary Professor in the University of Berlin (since 1834), and Member of the Prussian Academy of Sciences (since 1839), but, above all, the holder of an immense reputation for learning, as editor of Gilbert's *Annals of Physics and Chemistry*.

Poggendorff's father was a manufacturer in Hamburg, who had lost almost all his means through the French invasion, and had been unable in consequence to give his son a regular scientific education ; but the young Johann Christian's industry and talent made amends for this ; and a kindly helping hand extended to him by Dr. Runge of Berlin enabled him in 1823 to obtain the post of meteorological observer to the Prussian Academy of Sciences, after which his progress became rapid. He became editor of the *Annals* on Gilbert's death in 1824, and was awarded the honorary title of Professor in 1830, to which that of Doctor was added in 1834, when he was appointed Professor Extraordinarius. The *Annals* constituted a most monumental work, running at the year of J. C. Poggendorff's death in 1877 to 171 volumes. It contained contributions from the most eminent scientists of various countries, and was celebrated—and also feared—as Poggendorff's friend and biographer, Dr. W. Barentin, tells us, " for the careful choice that was made in the acceptance of articles. The care thus expended was vouched for by the celebrated, and feared, short notes, which were often added to the dissertations as suitable criticism, enclosed within square brackets, and signed ' P.' "

Reichenbach had prepared four short essays on " The Laws of Odic Light," with which he reasonably hoped to silence all the scoffers who maintained that the odic luminosity of bodies in the dark chamber was simply a figment of the sensitives' imaginations and the Baron's own credulity. They contained drastic proof of the contrary, as they reported on photographs actually taken by aid of the odic light alone, under scientifically arranged conditions and in the most intense darkness, by Günther, the photographer to the Royal Court in Berlin. The light proceeded from crystals, magnets, finger-tips, bodies affected odically by chemical reaction, friction, sound, and heat, masses of metal, and amorphous bodies charged with od. These essays, with plates of the photographs obtained, Reichenbach submitted early in 1861 to the redoubtable Poggendorff for insertion in his *Annals of Physics and Chemistry*.

Poggendorff accepted them, and published the first in due course in the March number of the *Annals*, vol. 112, p. 459, under the heading "Intensity of Light Phenomena." As the essays were studies on the feeblest degree of intensity of light known to exist, and the "relative" nature of its luminosity, namely, in the most intense degree of darkness alone, the publication was really an epoch-making event in the scientific world ; it was a study in "relativity," anticipating Einstein in a certain sense by more than half a century, and the heading affixed to it in the *Annals* seemed to show that the acute Poggendorff quite recognised the fact. Moreover, not a stricture appeared within square brackets signed " P."

But the other three essays failed to follow on ; and late in the year Reichenbach travelled all the way to Berlin to find out the reason why. Whether or not he saw Poggendorff in person about it I do not know ; but I infer not, as his words are (*Odic Events*, p. 53) : " I got to Berlin late in the year (October, 1861), and learned that the other three essays could not be accepted, because the matter contained in the first had excited too much displeasure among the Berlin physicists. But if I would consent, so I was told, to give a demonstration of the alleged phenomena before a number of the Berlin professors with the relative experiments, and were successful in establishing actual proof, then the publication of my essays could (*sic :* not ' would ') be taken up once more and continued."

The Baron took the slight in good part and with evident simplicity of soul, and began a round of visits to all the professors of physics, who were mostly, he tells us, old friends and acquaintances of his own, who had grown grey with him during the preceding thirty years. They showed him every courtesy ; but the Baron could not help noticing with surprise that for od and all relating thereto they had nothing to offer but the most ominous silence. " Whenever I began to touch on the subject," he writes, " I felt at once that I was harping on a string of an unpleasant tone. They coupled od and sensitivity in their minds with the so-called ' animal magnetism ' and ' mesmerism '; and with that all sympathy was at an end." He endeavoured to explain that he had no connection with these systems, that he wished to bring forward a series of quite newly observed facts, which as something objective had a right to a *locus standi* within the domain of physics, and that his object was not to preach mesmerism, but to submit the odic phenomena whose *de facto* occurrence he had certified in accordance with the rules of science to the test of actual examination by professional scientists.

These expostulations fell on deaf ears—to his exceeding great surprise. " To all, I said," he writes (*loc. cit.*, p. 54), " I only received evasive answers. I failed to see at the time, though I now see perfectly, that I might as well have ordered my carriage for the railway station." It was a prejudged affair: Mesmer had " queered the pitch " for the genuine scientist, and the professors—not too original or too strong-minded individuals, perhaps—were all afraid of being laughed at or thought " weird."

But the Baron was too big-minded to understand how such a thing as timidity or human respect could find a place in scientific circles ; and he persevered. He had been invited, practically challenged, to appear in Berlin, though they need not have invited him or challenged him. They may perhaps have thought, under the influence of the *Berliner Café-Klatsch* and professional banter, that the country cousin would never accept the challenge. But Reichenbach, with the naïveté of an Aquinas, or any

xxxvi LETTERS ON OD AND MAGNETISM

other genius noted for the quality by Schiller, took things literally. With such a man as himself the event of demonstration was bound to come off, and it did.

On the evening assigned, he tells us, Dr. Magnus the Rector, and Professors Dove, Poggendorff, Schellbach, and G. Rose, assembled in his dark chamber : all were professors of physics and allied sciences. He had intended to go through the whole series of photographic experiments with the various established foci of odic radiation, i.e. crystals, magnets, finger-tips, bodies affected by chemical reaction, friction, sound and heat, masses of metal, and amorphous bodies charged with od. But as soon as the first experiment with the crystal had been performed, and its photographic power demonstrated without objection on the part of anyone present, Professor Poggendorff created an unexpected diversion. He turned the photographic plate back to front over the peak of the crystal, so that the glass was next the mounting current of od, while the sensitized receiving-surface was on the other side of the glass. " If the so-called odlight is really light," said Poggendorff, " it must be capable of penetrating the glass, just as daylight does." The experiment was carried out so, and, lo, not a trace or mark appeared upon the sensitized surface !

It was baffling ; but Reichenbach had the presence of mind to try photography by daylight at once on two exactly similar plates, one presented in the ordinary way, and the other *à la* Poggendorff, back to front. The photograph was effected *through* the glass sure enough ; but it was notably weaker, and with a less sharp outline, than the one taken by direct daylight. The glass obviously checked or diverted a certain portion of the rays. Experimenting further, with the room once more darkened and the odlight substituted for daylight, it was found that the former would not penetrate even the very finest sheets of glass, nor even the very finest collodium and other films which Reichenbach brought into play. Poggendorff drew the conclusion that, as the odlight could not penetrate the ordinary transparent media which daylight did, it was not light at all in any true sense. He compared it with " Moser's invisible, latent " light. [*Dr. Georg Heinrich Moser* (1780–1858), *the eminent philologist of Ulm, and editor of the Oxford Plotinus, was said to be so familiar with his own library of* 15,000 *volumes that he could set his hand on any specified volume at once without a light—in the dark.*] Poggendorff's little joke !

The meeting at once broke up, without its members exhibiting the least curiosity to see the photographic effects of any of the other foci of odic radiation prepared by the demonstrator ! This was in April 1862.

The latter's discomfiture, however, only proved temporary. Left to his own scientific calm, he pursued to its logical end the observation just made *nem. con.*, that even daylight loses a portion of its rays and photographic power in penetrating a flat screen of glass. Working with Günther, the photographer, in the latter's studio, Reichenbach established without much trouble the ultimate photographic limit set by a glass medium to ordinary, strong daylight. It was found to be thirty-one plates of the description of glass known to the trade as " three-quarters white Nuremberg mirror-glass," which when set in close contact produced a total thickness of $6\frac{1}{2}$ inches (" Zoll "). Daylight penetrating this thickness of this quality of glass could not produce the faintest trace of an image on the sensitized surface, though the eye could see objects through the 6½-inch thick screen quite well. The *illuminating* rays of sunshine can consequently penetrate transparencies which set a dead block to the *chemically acting* rays. Our modern divers tell us that it is black dark at submarine levels to which they frequently descend, so that even the *illuminating* rays of sunshine find their term in an interposed transparent body such as sea-water. The whole story, in short, was one of " relativity."

Reichenbach had never lost his equanimity during the surprise that was sprung upon him, because he had had plenty of short-sighted, bespectacled sensitives in his dark chambers for years before, all seeing the odic flames quite clearly through their concave glass lenses. But he took the pains now to get together a number of proved sensitives in his dark chamber in Berlin, and made them look through thick panes of glass at his odic foci of various sorts. The luminous effect of the latter on their eyesight was just the same, or practically the same as before. To sensitives, then, observes the Baron with justice, it is no case of " latent " light, but " patent " light, patent and visible to all that particular class of sentient human beings who have the sensorium fine enough to discern in darkness so weak an apparition as the odic flame. I should like to know if there is any human sensorium—transferring the problem from the field of relative darkness to that of relative light—fine enough to discern the flame of an ordinary candle when held up in brilliant sunlight. Relativity —all along the line !

This difficulty out of the way, the Baron once more called his professors together—in the wording of his invitation, " to hear a lecture upon the subject of an unknown entity provisionally termed od and to witness illustrative experiments." He names those present : Geheimerath Mitscherlich, Geheimerath Ehrenberg, Professor Dove, Professor Riess, Professor Karsten, Professor Gustav Rose. His object this time was—leaving the specific subject of odic luminosity in relation to photographic power alone—to give a general, all-round demonstration, covering in brief, the whole subject-matter of the *Odic-Magnetic Letters*. For this purpose he needed the presence of suitably developed high-sensitives, a class of persons he had found in abundance in Vienna, and especially among the scientists themselves. But here in Berlin, to his surprise, and a good deal to his dismay, so he tells us, he had been unable, on his arrival in October 1861, to find a single sensitive among all the professors of natural science ! He had managed to come upon a few medical practitioners who were so gifted, but these had been rejected by the Berlin professors as incompetent witnesses in a matter touching general physics.

Upon this he had organized a search through the city for sensitives of any degree of power and in any class of life, but had had all the trouble in the world to find any, though he had even scoured the hospital wards for the purpose. He had fallen ill over the search, pursued through the rigours of a Berlin winter, and had been confined to his room for two and a half months. On recovery, he had approached persons reputed to be interested in " animal magnetism," and finally, after a world of trouble, had got together what he considered to be a sufficient number of sensitives for his purpose. On leaving the capital, however, in June 1862, it transpired that his nine months' search had only procured him 98 sensitives of all classes ! It did not seem the climate for the product.

From the account Reichenbach gives us of his second attempt at a demonstration before the professors of physics, I fancy that, not only was his own health too shaky, but that his hastily collected band of sensitives were not quite competent for his purpose. They appear to have been drawn rather from the lower and uneducated classes, and wanting in firmness and presence of mind when confronted in an atmosphere of learning with their superiors in education and social standing. Reichenbach himself was too much of a gentleman for a controversy of the rough and tumble sort that was eventually forced upon him ; he was too yieldingly polite to persons in high places, and too much, like Shakspere's Hamlet, " of a frank and open disposition," not to get into trouble thereby.

The trouble began half an hour before the meeting, when all the required apparatus, together with the sensitives, had been got properly into place, by an unexpected call from Professor Dove, a high luminary and power in the Berlin scientific world. This gentleman, assuming the language of command, gave the Baron peremptory notice that " *he would not permit him* " to give the lecture and demonstrations in accordance with the terms of the invitation issued, but that he himself, Dove, would take the investigation into his own hands and go to work with his own apparatus. Reichenbach tells us that he felt instinctively that the fate of the meeting was sealed by this exhibition of the " *Berliner Wind*,"— Berlin bluster, as we should say in English—but yielded, as Dove was such a very great man, and he himself so anxious to take Time by the forelock.

While Dove went off in quest of his " own apparatus," with which to conduct his " own investigation," the precise nature of which he did not for the moment disclose, Reichenbach filled up the time by conducting a few experiments with his sensitives—and quite successfully : (1) Pieces of metal secreted under the loose folds of a tablecloth were exactly located by their outflowing current to the hand of a high-sensitive passed over the cloth at a distance ; (2) A ball of wool held for eight to ten minutes in a professor's negative right hand, unknown to the sensitive, was correctly distinguished, by his odic polarity conveyed to the wool, from the positive odic character of a ball of wool which had been held in the same professor's positive left ; (3) Similarly, a glass of water held in a professor's right hand, unknown to the sensitive, was correctly distinguished by its pleasant (negative) taste from the unpleasant (positive) taste of a similar glass that had been held in the professor's left hand ; (4) A paper roll—an odically neutral medium—passed through a hole in a high drawing-room screen conducted positive and negative od, correctly recognized by the sensitive, from the touch of a professor's left and right hand respectively laid on the end of the roll, concealed from the sensitive's sight while the professor stood behind the screen ; (5) The same took place, though the effect was declared weaker, when Reichenbach merely approached his hand to the roll, without touching it, the sensitives on the other side of the screen giving correct pronouncements in each case as to whether the roll was approached by a left hand or a right.

Professor Dove now came in with a bagful of magnetic apparatus, and proceeded to test the sense of odic polarity in the sensitives by means of an electro-magnet. The non-professional reader may like to be reminded that an electro-magnet consists of a bar of soft iron, round which an insulated wire is wound in the direction of the motion of the hands of a clock, reading each successive section of the bar as an imaginary dial. If an electrical current from a battery be now passed through the wire in the direction just indicated, it converts the bar—by induction as the phrase is—into a temporary magnet, the south pole of which is at the end of the bar where the current begins and the north pole at the end where it passes off. The soft iron bar may be bent round, if desired, so as to form a horseshoe magnet. The great point to note about it is that the iron core only retains its character as a magnet so long as the electric current is passing, losing practically all its magnetization the instant the current ceases. Its character as magnet or non-magnet can thus be changed as quick as thought.

Moreover, by means of an apparatus called a commutator, the direction of the current from the battery may be reversed at will instantaneously, without changing the arrangement of the conductors from the poles ; that what one instant is the south pole of the magnet may the next instant become the north pole, and vice versa.

Now reflect on the fact shown by Reichenbach (Letter xiii., Odic Dualism) that iron, like all other metals, has its own odic polarity, and also on the fact, shown in Letter xvi., that the *velocity of odic conduction is,* when compared to the practically instantaneous velocity of electric conduction, *extremely slow.* According to the experiment cited in Letter xvi. od takes about 30 seconds to traverse 100 feet of iron wire, or three-tenths of a second per foot. In the case of a solid bar of iron, such as that of the electric magnet, it would travel still more slowly, especially when it is remembered that od does not glide along the surface like electricity, but permeates the substance of its conductor. (See Letter xii. on Odic Discharge and Conduction.)

Consequently when an electro-magnet is turned off and on, or reversed with rapidity, the odic characteristics have no time to establish themselves. Sudden changes (stoppages and activations) and sudden reversals of the electric current set as many changes and reversals of the odic conditions into a state of incipience, but not of progress or stability, and the result is an inextricable confusion between normal and electrically induced odic conditions, which no human thought or perception could follow, and which effectually prevents the acquisition of any definite character of odic polarity, though the magnetic polarity be there clearly defined a dozen times over.

The sensitive only judges of odic polarity by his sensations ; he does not judge of magnetic polarity. He may argue the presence of magnetic polarity from the presence of odic polarity ; but that argument proceeds from his faculty of reason, not from his faculty of sense. In short, he has no direct sense of magnetic polarity, and Reichenbach never maintained that he had. That is where Professor Dove made his mistake.

But consider the puzzling position in which the sensitives, ignorant of all these facts, must have found themselves when asked to declare their sensations in respect to this Protean monster of a magnet, which changed a pole from positive to negative and back again in a breath ! When Reichenbach himself had time to clear up his thoughts in the matter, it was easy for him to lay down the rule that, as a sequel to the slowness of odic conductivity, positive and negative od can co-exist in the same body for a relatively brief period, before either equilibrium or a definite polarity of a particular part be established. The presence of such a mixture, in a state of active change, must convey a mixed impression to the senses, and the sensitive must, paradoxically enough, answer his interrogator both Yes and No if he is to answer him with veracity. If he held consistently to either Yes or No, he would be practising a deception.

It is altogether to the credit, then, of Reichenbach's sensitives on this occasion that, when Dove with his devil's spoon was stirring up such a brew for their consumption, they blew hot and cold, as it were, with the same breath. They hesitated, answered one thing, then immediately contradicted it, then said they did not know, lost confidence in themselves, and broke down completely as witnesses. They must have said to themselves : How could I have felt so sure on former occasions ? Have I been deceiving myself all along, and imagining things ? What a striking demonstration of the accuracy of Reichenbach's observations in Letters xii., xiii., and xvi. !

Dove, no doubt, thought he had gained a victory and established fraud or self-deception in the sensitives. He had actually only succeeded in proving the erroneousness of the assumption that od is identical with magnetism, and therefore directly subject to magnetic laws.

Professor Dove's second experiment also seems to have been the result of undigested learning needing a corrective ; but he demoralized Reichenbach's sensitives by it still further, assigning them another physically impossible task. He produced a nickel bar-magnet with *consequent* poles, that is, poles occurring not merely at the two extremities of the bar, but intermediately also, and called upon the sensitives to locate their exact position by the sense of touch.

Here again, perhaps, the non-professional scientists among my readers may like to be reminded that what are called the poles of a magnet are its points of *maximum* magnetic intensity. It is found on analysis that *all parts* of a magnet and not merely the ends of the bar, are in a state of polarity ; so that our modern scientists state that the magnetic polarity belongs to each molecule throughout the bar. Take any magnet and break it in two, three, or more pieces, and it will be found that each piece is a complete magnet, with its own northward and southward poles. Now near, but not exactly at, each end of the magnet is to be found the *general result* of all the polarization in the body of the bar : it has been found convenient to refer to this point where the resultant force of the magnetization is observable as the *pole* of the magnet. It is the pole *par excellence* ; but every magnet is really full of intermediate poles, though we have not always instruments fine enough to recognize them with. But in some abnormal cases, for one reason or another, intermediate points will be found where polarity is readily, or definitely, perceptible, and these intermediate points of greater attraction and repulsion are called " consequent " poles, to distinguish them from the " chief " or " resultant " poles of the entire magnetic instrument.

Now the *perceptible* odic currents only emanate from the *resultant* poles of a metal magnet : theoretically, there may be somewhere in existence human sensitives with senses superlatively fine enough to recognize the od emitted by the consequent poles, as well as that emitted by the general, resultant poles of a magnet ; but such power is not claimed by Reichenbach. It is no answer to his claim, such as it is, to propose an experiment beyond the powers of his human odic magnetoscope : if a given thermoscope is not delicate enough to record some very fine trace of heat, it would be absurd to conclude that it is not a thermoscope at all. If the matter were to be pushed to its ultimate extreme, it would be as reasonable to expect the sensitive to be able to detect the polarity of every molecule in the body of the magnet, under pain of being regarded as a fraud or self-deceiver.

It is easy to explain all this quietly now, when the heat and dust of the scientific tournament have subsided, and Reichenbach admits in his *Odic Events in Berlin*, 1861–2, p. 35, that he was so confused, not to say intimidated, by Professor Dove's masterful, over-riding prowess in the lists, that he was neither in a condition for cool discussion, nor for reassuring the ladies of his following, whose hands trembled visibly with fright as they applied them to the magnet under the terrible professor's gaze. But he puts the matter in a nutshell in his book when he writes (*loc. cit.*, p. 34) : " The experiment ran counter to the laws of od. Its chief currents, strong enough, that is, for their polarity to be recognized, do not move laterally, but longitudinally, in bar magnets." And he had never maintained anything else. As it was, the sensitives employed in the case, finding themselves, to all seeming, suddenly deserted by their powers in a way they could not account for, took fright badly, and were led in a general rout by the highest sensitive of all, a lady not of the gentlefolk class, in whom most reliance had been placed, but who now hastily excused her presence to the awe-inspiring body of the Herren Professoren, and left the meeting in a fright.

It must not be forgotten, however, that, as recorded above, Reichenbach's first five experiments in this May meeting had been entirely successful, and, though conducted with the active co-operation of the professors present, had passed off without a single failure or hitch in all the reiterated trials, and without objection or questioning of the results on the part of the professors themselves. The facts had to be admitted, even if tacitly and unwillingly.

Reichenbach's demonstrations in Berlin, however stormy their career, had thus at any rate proved in principle the existence of a new force that called for scientific examination. He now concentrated his attention on proving the photographic phenomena to the satisfaction of the University professors, and for that purpose established himself in rooms in the University buildings, where he regularly carried on his investigations under their inspection, and to some extent with their actual co-operation and help. By the 2nd of June, 1862, he felt ready to face their highest circles once more, with apparatus and sensitives ready, and all explanations on the tip of his tongue, and issued invitations for the presence of the professors of physics in his dark chamber on the evening of 6th June.

He was surprised on that evening at the last moment to receive letters from all of them declining the invitation ; but, for the benefit of five persons interested in science who had attended—one a retired teacher of mathematics and physics of twenty years' standing, another an assistant-teacher of natural science, a third, president of a scientific society in Berlin, and two amateur scientists—he went through a series of experiments, though his two high-sensitives fled as soon as they learnt that the professors had declined the invitation and he could only use medium-sensitives for the purpose.

The chief experiment made was to show that the illuminating rays of od penetrated glass, though the odic rays did not. A Liebig hollow glass sphere containing still water was invisible to all the sensitives in the dark, but immediately became visible and filled with sparkling light as soon as the water was shaken, and so on. The guests present co-operated in every experiment, checking all to the best of their ability, which was considerable, and three of them, including the retired teacher, afterwards declared themselves convinced by the experiments of the existence of odic force.

At 10 p.m. that night the post brought the Baron a copy of the *Allgemeine Zeitung* of 4th June, in which he was amazed to read the following announcement made by the seven Berlin professors of physics in the form of a signed letter :

Allgemeine Zeitung, Wednesday, 4th June, 1862.

Mr. v. Reichenbach's Experiments in Berlin.— Baron von Reichenbach of Vienna has since 1845 made various publications on an alleged new natural force (*Agens*), which he considers he has discovered and to which he attaches the name of Od. He recently invited the undersigned during his stay in Berlin to experiments directed to establish the effects of this force, and then distributed printed reports giving an account of alleged successful experiments.

As the undersigned are named as witnesses of these experiments, and their names are in part so interwoven in the narrative as to make it look as though they agreed with Mr. v. Reichenbach's conclusions, they see themselves compelled, in order to avoid such a misunderstanding, to declare :

That the experiments shown them by Mr. v. Reichenbach have in nowise established what they were intended to show. Any proof of the existence of a new natural force consequently failed.

Berlin, 31st *May*, 1862.

EHRENBERG. G. MAGNUS. MITSCHERLICH. POGGENDORFF. RIESS. G. ROSE. SCHELLBACH.

" Cowardice ! " is Reichenbach's comment on the above. " Proof always fails—subjectively— if people will not listen to it ; but there it stands objectively all the same ! And to publish such a declaration, not in Berlin, but down in the south of Germany, in Augsburg ! And not even in a *scientific* paper, but in the most widely circulated *political* newspaper in Central Europe—obviously for the purpose of raising the widest possible prejudice against me by the crushing weight of numbers and official scientific position ! Is this consonant with professional etiquette and gentlemanly conduct ? " Is this Faraday's " honour of a scientist," he might have added.

With that he shook the dust of Berlin from his feet, and in that scientific dust lies buried the discovery of od to the present day.

But little remains to be added here. In 1862, when he met his rebuff in Berlin, Reichenbach was 74 years of age, but hale and hearty. He retired to Vienna, to his Castle of Reisenberg, where he never gave up his habits of scientific work, and in 1866 we find him publishing his *Principles and Definitions of Sensitivity and Od* (*Aphorismen über Sensitivität und Od, von Freiherrn von Reichenbach, Phil. Dr., Wien*, 1866. *Wilhelm Braumüller, kk. Hof- und Universitätsbuchhändler*). It had originally been limited to a few hundred copies distributed gratis in scientific circles, and bore the fighting dedication : " To the Seven Sages of Berlin (*Den gelehrten Berliner Sieben*), Messrs. Ehrenberg, Magnus, Poggendorff, Riess, G. Rose, Schellbach, and the Manes of Mitscherlich, who according to the Augsburg *Allgemeine Zeitung* of 4th June, 1862, are not clear in their minds as to the nature of Od, this book is respectfully dedicated—for their encouragement—by the Author."

His *Odic-Magnetic Letters* (*Odisch-Magnetische Briefe*, Cotta, Stuttgart, 1852) had been reprinted in 1856, marked " First Series : Second Edition." No " Second Series " was ever issued, **nor did Reichenbach ever withdraw or modify up to his death in 1869 anything in the book now before the reader.** The *Aphorisms* contain, however, an important amplification of its teaching as to the odic current from the live human subject, growing plants, peaks and cleavage planes of crystals, poles of magnets, etc. (See Letter v. and alibi.) He refers sometimes to this current or emanation as " die odische Lohe," *the odic glow*, and states in the course of the *Aphorisms* that it is the radioactive matter by means of which therapeutic effects are obtained by " passes " of a *highly sensitive* operator's hands over a patient, and by means of which certain mechanical effects also take place in movable objects when subjected to its flow from the body of *strongly sensitive* persons.   This odic " emanation," " glow," or " current," is very possibly what modern " spiritualist " or " spiritist " writers refer to under the perhaps unnecessarily learned and repellent name of " ectoplasm," coined from the Greek *ekto*, outside ; and *plasma*, paste or figment, when, in virtue of certain conditions not yet thoroughly cleared up, its subtle substance becomes congested and compacted into a paste.   Reichenbach does not call the odic flame or current an " aura " (Latin :

breath of air, airy current), though modern psychists frequently use that word, apparently as an equivalent for *his* " glow " (*Lohe*), or " current " (*Strömung*).

What the Baron had to say about this odic current, emanating from both organic and inorganic bodies, but with especial force from the bodies of certain " high-sensitives," i.e. strongly sensitive subjects, was, I suspect, to have been the subject of his unpublished " Second Series " of *Odic-Magnetic Letters*. But, as he came to publish the volume of *Aphorisms* in 1866, and as this volume, written in the same popular style as the *Letters*, covered the subject fairly completely, I fancy he was content to leave the matter so, only promising in his Preface to bring out without much further delay a methodical treatise *On the Odic Flame and the Mechanical Action of Od*. This, he said, would be taken from six lectures he had recently delivered before the Imperial Academy of Sciences in Vienna. It was published in Vienna in due course, in 1867, under the title of *Die odische Lohe und einige Bewegungserscheinigungen als neuentdeckte Formen des odischen Prinzips in der Natur.—The Odic Glow and certain Phenomena of Movement as newly discovered Forms of the Odic Principle in Nature*. It is not to be found in the British Museum library.

Meantime, for the purpose of absolutely completing the *Odic-Magnetic Letters* as a comprehensive popular summary of the doctrine set forth by Reichenbach in the whole course of his learned and voluminous works, I shall here add two brief extracts from the *Aphorisms*, giving the gist of what their author has to say about the aura or proto-ectoplasm : first, as to its *prima facie* phenomenon, and secondly, as to the use which he considers is made of it in " table-turning," for which, it will be seen, he does not in any way postulate the presence or action of disembodied human beings :

THE HUMAN AURA

" In somewhat shaded light, say in a room where the brilliancy of day has become enfeebled by the sky being overcast, or in evening candle-light, let a man hold his hand before his eyes at ordinary seeing distance. Then let him look at his fingertips, holding them against a dark background distant a step or two.

" Most men will see nothing unusual under such circumstances. But there will be a few among them everywhere who make an exception. These, on their attention being drawn to the matter, will, by looking narrowly, make out over the tip of each finger an extremely delicate current, colourless, non-luminous, like air, subject to motion, a few lines ['*Linien*': *prob. lines of print are meant = Zeilen : so far as I know, there is no division of the German inch, Zoll, into eight lines, as in English measure*] high, going upwards, inclining towards the south, and following the fingers wherever they are turned. It is not smoke, nor vapour [*Duft*], nor steam [*Dunst*] ; it looks like a fine flame, resembling—but notably more delicate in appearance than—an ascending body of heated air. . . .

" People who are able to see this are to be found easily and everywhere, are just as numerous among the agricultural classes and operatives as among office workers and drawing-room loungers, and are as frequent among men as women. They occur frequently among those who are restless in their sleep, or talk in their sleep, suffer a deal from headaches, are constantly troubled by cold feet, combine a decided preference for blue with a pronounced dislike of yellow, and among many of those who are commonly spoken of as ' nervous.' There is scarcely a good-sized house in town or country which does not number one or two such people among its inhabitants.

" The superficial objection has been often heard that the phenomenon is merely the result of the heat of the fingers, air rarefied by heat, which streams upwards in the vapour of perspiration. But the flames in question rise not only from warm fingers but from cold bodies as well [*including cold fingers, he might have added*], from leaves and blossoms, from the peaks of crystals, from the poles of magnets, from rods held with one end in sunshine, from the brims and stems of wine-glasses in which chemical reactions are taking place, from the rims of bells when struck, from strings yielding a musical tone, from the tapering ends of bodies under friction, from glass and metal rods heated at one end, from rheophores [*Gr.: ' current-carrier,' a general name given by Ampère to the conductor joining the poles of a Voltaic cell*] when working, from charged Leyden jars, from the free ends of bars of all metals, from surfaces of water, and in fact from the free end of all extended bodies whose other end has been immersed for a minute in any focus of radiation [' *Lohquell,' literally, ' source of glow* ']; finally, from countless other objects in which any kind of molecular dislocation takes place. The glow of the fingers; consequently, does not derive its existence from the heat of the blood, or perspiration of the skin, but has an independent existence. And it is perceived from all the above sources by the class of persons referred to, so soon as they bring it before their eyes in the way laid down above." *Aphorisms*, 1866, pp. 1–3.

MOTIVE POWER OF THE AURA

A. Pendulum Movements : In order to dissipate popular errors and superstitions connected with the pendulum, Reichenbach describes in his *Aphorisms* (p. 62 *sq.*), how he constructed a small pendulum free to move under a glass shade which cut off the influence of air-currents, but which left a small aperture at the top through which a finger could be laid on the motionless portion of a long string wound round a windlass with a little ball of lead suspended at the free end of the string. He found that he himself and all ordinary persons could produce no movements whatsoever by touching the fixed end of the string.

He was about to do away with his apparatus, thinking he had effectually disproved a source of popular superstition, when he chanced to ask a high-sensitive to lay his finger on the touch-point. Decided and unmistakable swinging of the pendulum resulted. Further experiments convinced him that all sensitives, and sensitives alone, possessed this power, the length of oscillation in the pendulum depending on the degree of sensitiveness, low, medium, or high, in the operator, and also on the state of the operator's health. He gives further detail as follows :

" If the right hand of a sensitive produce 8-line oscillations, and another right hand be laid upon it, diffusing like od, the oscillations are increased to 12 lines. If a left hand be laid on the operator's right, the motion of the pendulum at once ceases. If odically negative matter, such as selenium, sulphur, charcoal, etc., be placed in the operator's left, the oscillations increase ; if the same be done with odically positive matter, such as iron, copper, tin, lead, the pendulum stands still at once.

" If the operator has a watch, a key, or coins in his pocket, he is unfitted thereby to produce oscillations, no matter how high his degree of sensitivity. On one occasion I made an operator who had got rid of all metals on his person and produced 10-line oscillations, pull on boots with iron nails in the soles, and his pendulum came to a standstill at once. . . .

" The negative od takes its course from the sensitive's hand along the cord, which should not be too fine, and down to the plummet, which I had made 6 oz. in weight, diffuses a visible glow along the cord and around the plummet, is odically luminous in the dark chamber, and causes rectilinear oscillations proportionate in length to the amount of od discharged."

B. " **Table-turning** " [*Aphorisms*, pp. 64–71] :
[p. 64.] " I have often repeated a small experiment with all sorts of persons in Vienna and Berlin, which must be classed along with the phenomena of odic movement. A small visiting-card, or half a playing-card, in many cases even a fairly long scrap of paper, was set on the tip of a finger of the right hand, so as to balance. With non-sensitives and even medium-sensitives it always remained quite steady. But with the higher-sensitives, without exception, it soon began to turn round in jerks. . . . The movements succeeded better with the card on top of all five finger-tips set together. They went in short jolts forwards, then unexpectedly a few jolts backwards, then again forwards. All the time flame was seen streaming abundantly from the four corners of the card. In the dark the whole card comes out luminous, diffusing a beautiful, bright odic smoke from its

four corners, proceeding more strongly from the corners more distant from the body and more feebly from the corners nearer.

"In every case I regarded this occurrence of 'card-turning' as the boundary-mark of the higher sensitivity."

Reichenbach observed the same phenomenon with crystals (p. 65) and rod-magnets (p. 66), (5 inches long and 3 x 4 lines section, and 6 in. long with a 2 x 6 lines section), held lightly between the thumb and index-finger of **high**-sensitives for a minute or so. In the magnet experiment, he says :

"If I placed the sensitive with his face turned to the south, so that the rod of the magnet was parallel with the meridian, and its north-seeking pole turned away from the sensitive's body, and thus struggling to turn round northwards towards the sensitive, I was surprised to see it turn towards the south pole of the earth's axis, with its north-seeking pole forward and outward, away from the sensitive. Thus, contrary to its most fundamental law, the rod-magnet turned with its north-seeking pole, not to the north pole but to the south pole. In the case of one and the same pole, there we have the magnetic force tending to the north and the odic force tending to the south, and in this conflict the victory is with od, which dominates the magnet, and carries it captive along with it in the direction of the south." [*See confirmation of this by Dr. G. T. Fechner, infra*, p. x.]

Reichenbach then expresses his hope to be able to reconcile the public, who allege the fact of "table-turning without muscular action," with certain physicists who deny it :

" I hope by the following lines to act as an intermediary of peace ; though, unfortunately, in doing so I am unable to spare my learned colleagues for drawing down the blinds upon this subject in the faces of the non-learned but honest public, even though a Faraday himself should be their protagonist. [*Faraday had in June*, 1865, *constructed a small roller-apparatus to be placed underneath the hands of the sitters encircling the table experimented with, for the purpose of detecting fraud by its immediate registration of any muscular action exerted. He did, actually, render good service by detecting fraud in a notable instance by the use of this appliance, and published a long account of it in ' The Times' newspaper of 30th June, and ' The Athenæum' of 2nd July,* 1853.] I refer, as you no doubt suspect, to this unfortunate matter of table-turning. [*He then describes how he fixed a thick fringe of knitted wool handles a foot long to a table, which were taken hold of quite lightly (so as to maintain a visible slack loop in each handle) by a party of* **high**-*sensitives*.] All the same, the table came into motion after 40 to 50 minutes, and soon ran round so violently that, if anyone tried to hold it back by the fringe, it dragged him forcibly along with it. The principle of the motion flowed from the hands through the fringe into the table, and set it running, just as if the hands had lain directly upon it. It is consequently something that can be conducted and discharged. . . .

" But this movement, simply as produced and free from complication, never has a curvilinear, but only a rectilinear direction. *The tables do not dance, so long as they are only pulled in one direction.* It is only when a combination of forces, and a variety of impulses in different directions, are brought to play upon it, that the table falls into an irregular, rotatory movement from one point to another. And even then the movement is not a spinning one, and not a dance about its own axis, but an irregular tilting [*Treiben, lit. driving*] about from spot to spot (p. 70). If all the hands encircling a round table are pointed to the left, it turns to the left ; if all the hands are turned to the right, it runs to the right ; if a number of hands, are set round it irregularly in various directions, and if in addition to that the floor is not perfectly level, it staggers about, lifts itself up here and sets itself down there, and even plunges now and again in a circular direction."

The Baron had already described the luminous phenomena accompanying " table-turning " as done in his dark chamber [*Der Sensitive Mensch*, Bd. ii, s. 122], where he lays special stress upon the odic current proceeding from the *feet* of the sitters, in orange-coloured light from the left feet and bluish from the right, streaming round the feet and legs of the table and mingling with the similarly coloured currents proceeding from the sitters' hands and covering the top of the table. But he did not then suspect od to have been the source of the movement : it was only after the experience of his pendulum experiment (published for the first time in 1866) that he attributed the movements of " table-turning," etc., to odic force.

After the publication of *The Odic Glow* [*Die odische Lohe*] in 1867, Reichenbach, keen in spite of his 79 years, to promote the recognition of his work, left Reisenberg in the month of July and travelled to Leipsic, as the celebrated Dr. Gustav Theodor Fechner tells us in his *Memories of the Last Days of* the Odic Theory and its Originator [*Erinnerungen der Letzten Tage der Odlehre und ihres Urhebers, Leipzig, Breitkopf und Härtel,* 1876, pp. 8–9], for the express purpose of converting Dr. Fechner himself. Reichenbach, in spite of past controversies, had a high opinion of Fechner's essential impartiality and scientific standing, and wished to convince him of the mechanical motive power of the odic current. He remained in Leipsic, leading quite a lonely existence at the Hotel zur Stadt Dresden, till his death on 19th January, 1869, some eighteen months later.

Reichenbach had taken a single high-sensitive, Mrs. Ruf, a former housekeeper of Schloss Reisenberg, along with him; but she had been taken ill on the journey, and never recovered sufficiently to regain her abnormal powers. The Baron then undertook once more the weary work of collecting and observing sensitives in Berlin; but Fechner tells us they were mostly of the lower orders, engaged for hire, and, in Reichenbach's own judgment, unsatisfactory. None of them were high-sensitives. He endeavoured, nevertheless, by their help to satisfy Fechner that the odic current from a sensitive of average power could cause motion in an untouched pendulum; but perhaps through non-observance of his own strictly prescribed condition, viz. that only high-sensitives in full possession of their powers should be employed in this case, the experiment failed to answer expectations, and the pendulum remained unmoved. The Baron seems to have shown himself too eager, feeling that his time was short.

One experiment, however, conducted by Reichenbach with Mrs. Ruf in Fechner's presence, startled and impressed the latter so much that, with Reichenbach's ready goodwill, he repeated it under his own

conduct several times with all the scientific precautions that either he himself or Professor Erdmann,
his colleague at the University of Leipsic, could
devise.   In the result, he admitted unequivocally
that the conclusion was altogether in favour of the
possession of abnormal power by the sensitive—call
it odic power or by what name you will—quite
inexplicable by any scientific theory known to himself.
This was Mrs. Ruf's deflection of the magnetic needle
by attractive and repulsive passes made merely in
its vicinity by her fingers, hands, and even by her
elbows.   A single finger of her hand deflected a
one-inch needle enclosed under glass in an ordinary
compass-box to quite unmistakable extents, and
that repeatedly, under his own and Professor Erdmann's conduct of the experiment under the most
varied conditions and precautions, while Reichenbach
sat in a remote corner of the room.   The finger-tips
of one hand held closely together deflected the needle
from 40 to 50 degrees, while passes made with either
of her elbows deflected it as much as 90 degrees.
Mrs. Ruf, who was only convalescent, complained
that she was far from possessing her full powers on
these occasions, and Reichenbach, says Fechner,
told him that he had seen her cause the needle to
make a complete revolution through all the 360
degrees of the circle (see above, p. 56).

Fechner narrates in addition a considerable number
of other interesting experiments carried out by
Reichenbach in his presence with perfect success ;
but he also gives a few cases, comparatively very
few, in which the result seemed inconclusive, Mrs.
Ruf—who complained, however, of lack of power
through ill health—giving answers that did not
accord with the odic theory as Reichenbach himself
presented it.

There seems little doubt, so far as I can judge from Fechner's account, that, on the occasion of the pendulum experiment, the Baron let his eagerness to extend his theory so as to account for mechanical movement overcome his habitual scientific caution (see above, p. 54).

But then Fechner tells us that the eighty-year old man was at this time exhibiting unmistakable signs of senile decay. His sight was failing, and he was so deaf that shouting was required to make him hear. His legs could scarcely carry him, and he was finally struck with paralysis, hemiplegia, which put an end to his life after two days of unconsciousness. "Up to the last days of his life," Fechner writes (*op. cit.* p. 11), "he grieved at the thought of having to die without obtaining recognition for his system, and such was the tragic fate that actually befell him."

Current French and German opinion of a serious nature as to Reichenbach's scientific merit may be gleaned from the standard reference books of the two countries, both in regard to science in general and the as yet unrecognized science of od in particular. The relative passages are here reproduced in their integrity, so as to avoid all suspicion of garbling.

In the *Grande Encyclopédie* we read :

" His reputation as a savant was great in Germany. Chemistry, in particular, owes him several important discoveries, notably those of paraffin (1830), eupion (1831), creosote (1832), and pittacal (1833). He was the first to make known in an exact style the geological formation of Moravia.

[*He published his ' Geologische Mittheilungen aus Mähren '—' Geological Reports from Moravia '—in* 1834.]

" Finally, he devoted the latter portion of his life, which he spent in his castle of Reisenberg, near Vienna, to researches in animal magnetism and psycho-physical phenomena, and he claimed to have discovered a new natural force, od, which was, he held, the agent of our sensations. The theories which he set forth on this subject engaged him in lively controversies."

The judgment expressed in the *Allgemeine Deutsche Biographie* runs thus :

" Reichenbach has left a respected name as a researcher, and we owe him investigations in mineralogy, geology, and chemistry. The science of meteorites is due to him, and he bequeathed his fine collection of them to the Austrian nation.

[*Between* 1835 *and* 1860 *he published a long series of scientific papers on meteorites : see especially* ' *Ueber Blitz ohne Donner* '—' *On lightning without thunder,*' *Poggendorff's Annals, xliii,* 1838 ; *a long list of references to his papers on meteorites is given in Poggendorff's Biogr.-lit.* ' *Handwörterbuch.*'] He surveyed the districts of Brünn and Blansko, reporting in his *Geol. Mitt. aus Mähren—Geological Reports from Moravia—*Wien, 1834. Of still greater importance are his chemical researches, which are mostly in connection with his own technical products. Thus he discovered paraffin and creosote from coal-tar. These are not, of course, bodies in the chemical sense, and Reichenbach's research must also be regarded as incomplete ; but they are materials that have attained to great importance through their practical application.

" A series of other substances discovered by him, such as eupion, picamar, kapnomor, and assamar, met with less notice, and do not, in fact, deserve anything else, as, scientifically speaking, they are not characterized with exactitude and, practically, are without importance. On the other hand, the beautiful colouring materials produced by him from tar, cedriret and pittacal (eupitton acid), have recently [1888] undergone exact investigation at the hands of Liebermann and Hofmann, so that their chemical constitution is cleared up.

" Reichenbach was also known to a wider section of the public through his researches in the so-called Od. . . . [*Here his main findings are briefly stated.*] It must be confessed that he met with no applause from the learned world in the matter of these researches and views.; on the contrary, he was violently attacked on account of them (among others by Karl Vogt and Mole-schott), and even turned into ridicule. He did not, however, allow himself to be disquieted on that account, and went to live in Leipsic in order to procure a better reception for his views. After his death, which took place in that city shortly afterwards [1869], Od was no longer talked about, and to-day [1888] it is quite forgotten, although similar views have, of course, frequently come up since then under other names."

I shall now quote the opinion of the late eminent scientist, Dr. William Gregory, M.D., F.R.S.E., Professor of Chemistry in the University of Edinburgh, first, as to the Utility of Enquiry into the Subject of " Odic Force," and, secondly, as to the qualifications of Baron von Reichenbach as our guide in such an enquiry. I content myself with the transcription of two passages, bearing respectively on these two points, from his Preface to the English version of the thick, and somewhat unattractively technical, volume of the *Researches*, published in London and Edinburgh in 1850, but now quite out of print.

1. " First, as to the objects of enquiry. It may be safely laid down that no well-ascertained fact, or series of facts, can possibly exist in nature, which are not worthy of our earnest study. It is no answer to say that there are many facts of no practical value ; for the fallacy of such an assertion has been too often proved by the unexpected application of apparently trifling facts to important purposes, theoretical as well as practical. When Liebig and Soubeiran first described a peculiar volatile fragrant liquid produced by the action of bleaching powder on alcohol, this fact was recorded and stood for many years in our annals as a mere curiosity of science. Yet, when the time came, this insignificant compound, under the hands of my accomplished colleague, Dr. Simpson, started up into the highest practical value as CHLOROFORM. Had *all* the properties of this body been at first *carefully studied*, we should not have had to wait till 1846 or 1847 for this boon to suffering humanity. It would be easy to fill a volume with parallel cases, from the Steam Engine to Gun Cotton, all proving the great truth that no natural fact is insignificant or unimportant."

This reminds one of Benjamin Franklin's customary rejoinder to any query addressed to him as to the *utility* of a particular scientific fact—a rejoinder that Michael Faraday loved to make his own : " What is the use of a baby ? " We must wait and see, and watch him grow.

2. " The qualifications of the Author [Reichenbach] for such an enquiry are of the very highest kind. He possesses a thorough scientific education, combined with extensive knowledge. His life has been devoted to science, and to its application to the practical purposes of mankind. [*Here Gregory recounts R.'s achievements.*] In particular he is the highest living authority on the subject of meteorites or aerolites. . . . But these are the least of his qualifications. He has a turn of mind, observing, minute, accurate, patient and persevering in a rare degree. All his previous researches bear testimony to this ; and at the same time prove that he possesses great ingenuity and skill in devising and performing experiments ; great sagacity in reflection on the results ; and, more important than all, extreme caution in adopting conclusions ; reserve in propounding theories ; and conscientiousness in reporting his observations. He has been found fault with for too great minuteness of detail ; but this fault, if in such matters it be a fault, arises from his intense love of truth and accuracy ; a quality which, when applied to such researches as the present, becomes invaluable, and cannot easily be pushed to excess.
" It therefore appears that Berzelius, who well knew the value of the Author's labours, was right in saying that the investigation could not be in better hands. Having myself been familiar with the Author's writings, and in frequent correspondence with himself for twenty years, I have here ventured to add my humble testimony to that of the great Swedish philosopher."

A word now as to the scientific authority of Professor Gregory himself.

Dr. William Gregory (1803–1858), Professor of Chemistry in the University of Edinburgh from 1844 till his death on 24th April, 1858, is a representative of the *fifth* generation of a line of *nine* distinguished scientists, descended directly from the Rev. John Gregory, parish minister of Drumoak, Kincardineshire, Scotland. Our respect for the sturdiness and fine quality of this patriarchal oak is increased when we are told by Dr. Thomas Reid, the metaphysician, who was his biographer, that he was fined, deposed, and imprisoned by the Covenanters, and only died in 1653, after becoming the father of 32 children by two successive wives !

Nine scientists of the highest rank make up this wonderful line, and I make no apology for recording them as follows : (1) David (1627–1720), inventor, and his brother (2) James (1638–75), mathematician, sons of Rev. John Gregory of Drumoak ; (3) David (1661–1708), astronomer, son of David above, and brother of Charles and James, who were also fine mathematicians ; (4) David (1696–1767), son of David last mentioned, Professor of History and Modern Languages in the University of Oxford ; (5) John (1724–73), grandson of James the mathematician of 1638–75, Professor of Medicine in the University of Edinburgh, who was succeeded in his Chair by his son (6) James (1753–1821) ; (7) George (1790–1853), a most eminent physician, grandson of John of 1724–73 ; (8) William (1803–58), son of James of 1753–1821, Professor of Chemistry at the University of Edinburgh ; (9) Duncan Farquharson Gregory (1813–44), Fellow of Trin. Coll., Cam., mathematician. The lives of all nine are recorded in the *Dictionary of National Biography*, and are well worth the attention of the student of heredity.

It would be totally unfair to omit due mention of the matriarch of this race of scientific giants. She was Janet Anderson, daughter of the David Anderson of Finyhaugh who was nicknamed, from his versatility and energy, *Davie-do-a'-thing* (i.e. " do all things ") ; he was said to have constructed the spire of St. Nicholas's Church in Aberdeen, and to have removed the hill called Knock Maitland from the entrance to Aberdeen Harbour. Miss Agnes M. Clerke of Skibbereen, Co. Cork, the well-known historian of astronomy (1842–1907) and honorary member of the Royal Astronomical Society, remarks with perfect justice, in her sketch of the life of James Gregory, astronomer and correspondent of Sir Isaac Newton, that by the marriage of David Anderson's daughter, Janet, with the Rev. John Gregory of Drumoak " the hereditary mathematical genius of the Andersons was transmitted to the Gregorys and their descendants."

That genius persevered in the direct line for full 200 years, from 1658 to 1858, the year that marks the death of Professor William Gregory, Reichenbach's official introducer to the English-speaking world. I know no other such example of family genius perpetuated throughout two centuries in the whole history of science. I can only parallel it in the field of literature ; for in English literature the paramount genius of the O'Sheridans of Cavan distinguished itself just as remarkably, and for the still longer period of nearly three centuries, from the year that Sheamus O'Sheridan translated the English Bible for Bishop Bedell into Irish, about 1630, down to the days of the last literary descendants of Richard Brinsley Sheridan in our own time. The Macgregors and O'Sheridans can shake hands over that. Nara deifir idir a gclannaibh go deo! (*May there ne'er be a difference between their clans!*)

Here is Professor Gregory's

GENEALOGICAL TREE

Rev. John Gregory of Drumoak m. Janet Anderson.

Their Son	James (1638–75), F.R.S., Prof. Mathem. Univ. Edin., friend of Newton ; m. Mary Jameson.
,, Grandson	James (d. 1731), Prof. Medic. Univ. Aberdeen ; m. Anne Chalmers.
,, Great-grandson	John (1724–73), F.R.S., Prof. Medic. Univ. Edin. ; m. Elizabeth, d. of Lord Forbes.
,, Gt.-gt.-grandson	James (1753–1821), Prof. Medic. Univ. Edin.; m. Miss McLeod.

,, Gt.-gt.-gt.-gr'sons :

William (1803–58) Prof. Chem. Univ. Edin.	Duncan Farquharson (1813–44), F. Trin. Coll., Cam., mathematician.

William Gregory was born at Edinburgh on 25th December, 1803. He received a medical education, but had so strong a bent for chemistry that, after graduating at the University, he made it his speciality, and visited the Continent in pursuit of this study. He became extra-academical lecturer on chemistry at Edinburgh, lecturer at the Andersonian University, Glasgow, and lecturer at the Dublin Medical School. In 1831 he introduced a process for making muriate of morphia, since generally adopted. In 1839 he became Professor of Medicine and Chemistry in

King's College, Aberdeen, and in 1844 Professor of Chemistry at Edinburgh, occupying the Chair till his death on 24th April, 1858. He was thus only fifty-four years of age when he died, and in his later years, as he tells us himself, suffered from an affection of the lymphatic glands which caused painful swellings in his legs.

The cautious judgment of the *Dictionary of National Biography* upon William Gregory's life-work, contributed by G. T. Bettany, runs as follows :

" Having been a favourite pupil of Liebig at Giessen, Gregory did much to introduce his researches into this country, translating and editing several [*no less than seven*] of his [*principal*] works. His own chemical works were useful in their day, especially from the prominence they gave to organic chemistry. [' *Outlines of Chemistry*,' 1845, *2nd ed. 1847, published later in 2 vols.,* 1853, *as ' The Handbook of Inorganic Chemistry ' and ' The Handbook of Organic Chemistry ' respectively ; German ed. of latter, Brunswick,* 1854.] He was skilled in German and French, and kept well abreast of chemical advances on the continent. . . . Being compelled to adopt a sedentary life, he spent much time in microscopical studies, chiefly on the diatoms, and wrote a number of careful papers on the subject. His character was simple, earnest, and amiable. Some thought him much too credulous in regard to animal magnetism and mesmerism. His views have much in common with the recent theory of telepathy."

The writer of this, the late Mr. G. T. Bettany, stops short, it will be observed, at passing any judgment

himself upon Gregory's alleged beliefs of alleged
occurrences in the domain of *Animal Magnetism*
and *Mesmerism* without sufficient evidence.   But,
on perusal of the fourth edition of Professor Gregory's
book, *Letters to a Candid Inquirer on Animal Magnetism,* 1851 (*4th ed., George Redway, London, 1896,
published under the title " Animal Magnetism, or
Mesmerism and its Phenomena," with an Introduction
by " M. A., Oxon."—The Rev. Stainton Moses, a
well-known " spiritualist "*), I find that, with a few
absolutely trifling exceptions, the whole work is
taken up with the professor's *own personal observations*
and reports of cases, which are detailed throughout—
(with perfectly punctilious scientific precision)—as
seen with his own eyes and presented directly to the
perceptive faculty of his own brain.   There is no
room, then, for any question of credulity or in-
credulity in the case.   The reports constitute first-
hand evidence.   The only questions that, in my
opinion, could be scientifically raised in the matter of
reports emanating from a scientist of such standing
are : Was Professor Gregory in normal, healthy
control of his senses when drawing up these reports,
or was he not ?   If he was, then could he be trusted
morally to tell the truth ?   Every man, especially
every scientist, deserves to have such questions
touching sanity and honour answered in the affirma-
tive until the negative be proved.   Mr. Bettany's
action in including in a serious life-record such a
sentence as the above, beginning " Some thought,"
seems to me, therefore, to be indefensible, and the
sentence should, in my opinion, be simply struck out
of the evidence as impermissible before passing any
judgment on the case.

After careful perusal of Professor Gregory's reports
and comments on the subjects in question, my own

udgment is that he was not all a credulous man, but exhibits, on the contrary, **the scientist's instinct of limiting himself strictly to the observation of fact and drawing therefrom no more than the inevitable conclusion, and that only provisionally.** Thus he writes at the conclusion of his book (*Animal Magnetism*, p. 252 and *ult.*) :

" I must now conclude, and I would do so by once more pointing out that my object has not been to explain the facts I have described, but rather to show that a large number of facts exist which require explanation, but which can never be explained unless we study them. I am quite content that any theoretical suggestions I have made should be thrown aside as quite unimportant, provided only the facts be attended to. . . . But I think we may regard it as established : first, that one individual may exercise a certain influence on another, even at a distance . . . tenthly, that not only the human body, but inanimate objects, such as magnets, crystals, metals, etc., etc., exert on sensitive persons an influence identical, so far as it is known, with that which produces mesmerism ; that such an influence really exists, because it may act without a shadow of suggestion, and may be transferred to water and other bodies ; and lastly, that it is only by studying the characters of this influence, as we should those of any other, such as electricity or light, that we can hope to throw light on these obscure subjects. Let us in the meantime observe and accumulate facts ; and whether we succeed or not in tracing these to their true causes, the facts if well observed and faithfully recorded will remain, and in a more advanced state of science will lead to a true and comprehensive theory."

I conclude from the foregoing evidence, taken in its totality and in its detail, that Professor William Gregory is a fit and proper person to vouch to the English reader for the high scientific authority of Baron Carl von Reichenbach, and that, in fact, a fitter or more proper person for any such fiduciary office in the public intelligence department of science it would be impossible to conceive.

LETTERS ON
OD AND MAGNETISM

Whatever is true is a power, not so much because it is said
as because it is the truth.—ANONYMOUS.

Augsburg *Allgemeine Zeitung*

AUTHOR'S PREFACE

THESE letters on od have been reprinted, with very few changes, from the *Allgemeine Zeitung* of Augsburg. Their object, speaking plainly, was to appeal to the German public against the unfair dealing of certain professional members of the learned world, who brought no argument but their scientific reputation to bear upon the task of declaring researches of the present day untrustworthy *à priori* and bringing them into contempt at the bar of public opinion by loftily condemning them as bereft of foundation in fact.

Everything that is new has to fight its way against whatever is old. The mere discomfort of having to make room for a stranger arouses the spirit of opposition. But I am no victim of self-delusion. Many of the facts I have adduced are known to the entire world : they hold their ground hard and fast against all logical attack, and hundreds of thousands of the German people bear witness to them. The conclusions drawn from them are practically self-evident, and public opinion, with its instinct for the truth, has in all quarters received my work with benevolent attention.

That discussions of this nature should, in a political newspaper, be restricted to summary presentment, follows as a matter of course from the mixed nature of the circle of readers addressed. A few leading statements, these made as clearly as possible, and anything like expatiation banned, are all that space permits. We have often, in previous issues of the *Allgemeine Zeitung*, been treated to serial letters on astronomy, chemistry, geology, phrenology, and

3

physiology ; but, in spite of that, my letters have stood in a position of obvious disadvantage. Letters on the subjects quoted merely dealt with truths already known or recognized, truths which no one contested ; but letters on the subject of od introduce entirely new matter, as well as new points of view on matters already known, so that they find themselves subject to the necessity of not merely asserting, but also frequently of being called on to prove. Letters of the former class proceed along the beaten highway, while those of the latter must make a clearing for their own use through the thorny thickets of controversy.

Such must be my preface to the letters now laid before the reader, and I must refer those who require more ample details of exposition, more rigorous proofs, and more fundamental treatment, to the work I have already published : *Researches on Magnetic Force, etc.*, while bespeaking their patience for a short time, till I have, as I hope, concluded a larger work, reporting the further investigations I have been engaged on for some time past, and taking in more extensive researches than could be dealt with in the form of letters.

REICHENBACH.

Reisenberg Castle, near Vienna.
August, 1852.

CONTENTS

[*Translator's notes within square brackets.*]

LETTERS ON OD AND MAGNETISM

[By Baron Carl von Reichenbach]

I

Sensitives

HAVE you never in your life, dear reader, come across people with the strange fancy of disliking everything yellow, and yellow itself as a colour? . . .

One would think that a beautiful lemon, a resplendent gold, a fiery orange, was something charming to look at. Where can the feeling of aversion come in? And ask this same class of people what colour they *do* like, and they will all answer as with one mouth: blue.

Certainly, the azure of the celestial deeps is a sight to do one good. But when evening frames the azure in gold, then surely the beautiful becomes something more than beautiful and merges into the magnificent. Had I to choose between spending the rest of my days in a maize-coloured or a sky-blue room, I should probably, of the two colours named, prefer the yellow; but all the anti-yellowites to whom I have ever said so have always laughed at me, and pitied my taste.

Well now, I invert the question; I ask you to tell me if you have ever met a man who said he could not endure blue. Never, to a certainty. Never has anyone been found who abominated blue. Whence comes it, now, that a certain class of mankind agree in their dislike of yellow, and all agree in their liking for blue ?

Colour-physics teach us that yellow and blue stand in a certain mutual relationship : they are complementary colours, occupying as it were opposite poles. Is it possible that underneath this fact something else lies hidden than the mere effect of the colour upon our eyesight ? Some more fundamental difference than the mere optical difference of colour familiar to all of us, some difference which escapes our senses ? And could there be appropriated to the perception of such a difference a difference also of human faculty, a difference to the effect that some might be able to perceive what is unrecognizable by others ? Could there be, so to speak, men with two sorts of senses ? That would be a somewhat peculiar state of affairs. Let us try and get further into it.

A girl, we may take it, is well enough pleased to see herself in the looking-glass. And perhaps, also, there are men who take pleasure in the reflection of their own dear selves. And who could begrudge them the pleasure, when a successful copy of God's fair masterpiece smiles back upon them, and awakens anticipatory joy in the conquest which already flushes their cheek ? Is there anything in life more glorious or beatific than the beautiful Myself ?

How would it be though—and it might really be possible—if there were girls, women, men, who shy off mirrors ? Who turn away and cannot bear to see themselves in one ?

In very truth there are such persons. There are men, and not a few in number, who are caused a peculiar feeling of distress by a looking-glass, as though some sickly, repellent emanation came to them from it, so that they cannot stay quiet there for a minute. It is not merely their own portrait that the mirror throws back to them ; it returns them also some indescribable, painful sort of impression, which some feel more and others less, while to others it is only just so far perceptible as to leave them with a definite dislike of mirrors. What is this ? And what does it come from ? Why do some men only experience this feeling of repulsion ? Why not all ?

No doubt you have often travelled ; and so it cannot but be that you have come across people in the mail coach, omnibus or railway-carriage, who with the most aggressive selfishness, wherever they may be, insist on throwing open the carriage windows. Be the weather as bad as may be, blowing a hurricane or as cold as ice, they will show no consideration for their fellow-travellers' rheumatism, but conduct themselves insufferably. You have regarded this as bad form ; but I ask you to postpone your judgment a little—at any rate until a few more of my letters have come into your hands. They will succeed, perhaps, in convincing you that, within the confined limits of a " present company," things whose nature is still unrecognized are wont to happen, things strong enough to be quite irresistible to many of the persons who form that company, while others have not the faintest sense of their existence.

Is it possible that among all your friends you have none whose crank it is never to sit between others in a row, be it at table, in the theatre, in society, or in church, but who always wants the corner-seat for himself, always elects to be fugleman of the file ? Take note of him ; he is our man ; we shall soon come to closer acquaintance with him.

You will be sure to have known ladies who often feel faint in church, though otherwise their health is quite good. You may give them the corner-seat, but even there they will feel faint, and sometimes have to be carried out in a swoon. If you pay any attention to the matter, you will find that it is always the same, that is, only a certain class of persons who are taken this way. They are absolutely incapable of sitting any length of time in the nave of a church without growing faint, and yet they are otherwise healthy people.

Your doctor will tell you that, if you want a good, sound sleep, you must lie on your right side. Do you ever ask him why? If he is an honest man, he will say he does not know. He is ignorant of the cause ; but he does know from his varied experience that there are many persons who never can get to sleep when lying on their left side. His patients have often told him that, but what is really at the bottom of the fact is unknown to him.

If you care to go more closely into the matter, you will find out that it is not *all* men who have to lie on their right in order to get to sleep, and that very many people sleep habitually on their left ; you will find, in fact, that there are plenty of people who are quite indifferent as to how they go to sleep, right or left, and to whom a night's repose on the left ear brings just as much refreshment as one on the right. But you will also find that those who cannot sleep on their left, but only on their right, make a minority so subject to this peculiarity as a class that they can lie on their left hour after hour, even half the night long, without getting to sleep, while so soon as they turn round in bed on to their right side they get off to sleep in a moment. It is certainly a very peculiar thing ; but you can observe it in all the countries of Europe.

How many people are there who cannot suppress a feeling of disgust when they make use of a fork of German silver at table, or a fork made of argentan, " new silver," Chinese silver, or whatever else such compositions may be called, while others cannot imagine why the compositions should make such a difference from genuine silver as not to be fitted for use on ordinary occasions? How many persons are to be met with who simply could not endure coffee, tea, or chocolate made in a brass kitchen utensil, while most other people would never notice the difference?

How many people, again, have an aversion from hot food, especially overcooked food, from rich dishes also and sweet dishes, and infinitely prefer cold and simple foods, and especially such as are slightly on the side of acidity? No small number among these persons evince so extraordinary a liking for salad that they may be heard to remark that they would give up the rest of the menu for the salad alone. Others are unable to imagine how so unqualified a preference could exist.

There are some people who simply will not endure having anyone else standing close behind them; they avoid popular gatherings of all sorts, crowds, and markets. Others find it disagreeable to take another by the hand, and absolutely unbearable for anyone else to retain for any length of time the hand they themselves proffer; if they cannot get it free otherwise, they will wrench it away. Then how many people are there not who cannot bear the heat from an iron stove, but feel quite comfortable when it proceeds from one of stonework?

Must I continue? Must I go on enumerating for your hearing hundreds of other such reasons to excite our wonder at the attitude of a certain well-defined class of individuals?

Well, what are we to think of it all? Is it simply a case of imagination and neglected education, or bad habits occasioned, perhaps, by local disturbances of an otherwise healthy equilibrium? It may seem so, of course, to those who only take a superficial view of the matter; and unfortunately such seeming has only too often led people into facts of injustice towards such sensitive persons as those I have described. Were these peculiar phenomena verified only in particular instances, scattered as chance occurrences among different individuals in varying situations, there might perhaps be some justification for regarding them as of small importance. But one remarkable circumstance, which up to the present day has not been considered worthy of attention, sets the matter on quite a different footing: all the peculiarities attributed to these persons are not found in them as individuals, but in every case as *in a class*.

When you trouble to investigate, you find most, and frequently all, of the peculiarities mentioned in one and the same individual; but never, not one single time, do you find one only by itself. The foe to yellow shuns the looking-glass; it is the man in the corner-seat who flings the window open; the right-side sleeper is the one who gets faint in church · the people who are disgusted by brass and German silver like cold and simple eatables and are fastidious over fat and sweets; it is they who are fond of salad, and so on; in every case the whole unbroken series of likes and dislikes is to be found in the same person, from hatred of yellow down to disinclination for sugar, and from fondness for blue down to keen appetite for salad. There is a *solidarity* uniting all these wonderful peculiarities in their possessor;

experience shows this on all sides ; whoever has one of the list has, as a rule, all the others too.

The conclusion is clear : there is a connection between them all which cannot be refused recognition ; and, if that is so, it can only be because they are all related in turn to a fundamental bond of union, to a hidden secret source, from which they all proceed in common. Now if this source be present in some men and absent in others, it is obvious that, taken from this point of view, there are in effect two classes of men : ordinary men, who have none of all these faculties of sensibility, and those peculiarly subject to excitation, who are excited in the way already described on every trifling occasion.

The latter class may be called " Sensitives " ; for they are, in fact, frequently more sensitive than a mimosa. They are so in the very depths of their nature, a nature they can neither lay aside nor treat with arbitrary violence ; and whenever their peculiarities have been taken for cranks and contrariness their feelings have always been hurt by the fact. They have quite enough to suffer without that from our everyday world, which has never hitherto taken any account of them. Their sufferings are the consequence of their hitherto unrecognized peculiarity in the sensory faculty, and they are entitled to more consideration than has hitherto been accorded them. Their number is not small, and we shall soon see how deeply human life is penetrated by these peculiar factors, of which I have now given you only the most elementary and superficial sketch.

II

Od—Crystals—The Dark Chamber

You have already succeeded, I dare say, by means of the distinctive marks I have given you, in finding out some of your acquaintance whom the characteristics fit, those whom I called sensitives. In point of fact it is not difficult to lay one's finger on them ; they are to hand everywhere in great numbers. And if you cannot at once get hold of some in quite good health, then turn your attention to those who pass restless nights, who are always pulling the bedclothes about during their sleep, who talk, or even get out of bed while dreaming, are greatly troubled by passing attacks of sick headache, frequent sufferers from stomach-aches of short duration, complain of nervous depression, are not fond of large parties, and like keeping to a few friends, or even seek for solitude. All such people are, with few exceptions, of a more or less sensitive nature.

What I have recounted, however, only makes up the trivial aspect of the matter on which you are consulting me ; as soon as our subject is laid on the touchstone of science, things of quite other importance come into view. Just procure a natural crystal, as big a one as you can get, say a gypsum spar two spans in length, a heavy spar, or a St. Gothard mountain crystal a foot long, and lay it horizontally over the corner of a table or the arm of a chair, so that both ends project unsupported. Now lead a " sensitive " person up to it, and tell him to put the palm of his left hand within three, four, or six inches' distance from each end of the crystal, one end after the other ; it will not be half a minute before he will tell you that a fine, cool current is coming against his hand from the end of the upper part of the peak of the crystal, while from the other end—but on the lower, broken surface, that on which the crystal grew—a certain feeling of lukewarmness reaches his hand. He will find the feeling of coolness pleasant and refreshing, that of the lukewarmness unpleasant, and accompanied by a disagreeable feeling, one almost of disgust, which, after a short period, will affect his whole arm, if kept there, and produce a sort of feeling of lassitude.

When I first made this observation, it was just as novel as puzzling ; nobody, wherever I went, would believe it. Meantime I have repeated it with hundreds of sensitives in Vienna ; it has been confirmed in England, Scotland, and France ; and anyone can easily put it to the proof himself, as sensitives exist everywhere. When they hold their hand near other parts of the crystal, say the bevelments on each side, they do, it is true, feel the two sensations of coolness and lukewarmness, but to an incomparably weaker degree than at the two ends, which are opposite poles. Non-sensitives feel nothing at all.

As these contrasting sensations are excited without the crystal being touched, and at a distance of several inches—in fact, in the case of strongly sensitive persons at a distance of several feet—it seemed to be that from these so-to-speak semi-organic stones something was proceeding, emanating, radiating, something as yet unknown to natural science, something which, however incapable we may be of seeing it, still makes its existence known through its effects upon the body. Now sensitives being, so far as *feeling* is concerned, so very much more capable than other men, the thought occurred to me that they might, in certain respects, be superior to us also in *the sense of sight*, and perhaps be able, in dense darkness, to perceive something of these peculiar emanations from crystals.

To put this to the proof, one dark night in May 1844 I took an immensely large mountain-crystal with me on a visit to a highly sensitive girl, Miss Angelica Sturmann ; her doctor, Professor Lippich, a man celebrated as a pathologist, was present on the occasion. We put two rooms into complete darkness, and in one of them I placed the crystal, in a spot unknown to the others. After pausing a little, to allow our eyes to get accustomed to the dark, we brought the girl into the room where the crystal was. Only a short time elapsed before she told me the place where I had set it down. The whole body of the crystal, she said, was glowing through and through with a fine light, while a body of blue light, the size of one's hand, was streaming out of its peak, in constant motion to and fro, and occasionally emitting sparks ; it was tulip-shaped, and disappearing in fine vapour at the summit.

When I turned the crystal round, she saw a dense red and yellow smoke rising over the butt-end. You can imagine how delighted I was with this statement. It was the first observation of thousands of others similar to it, which followed on from that day to this, made with crystals under innumerable variations of conditions, observations which, through the medium of a multitude of sensitive persons, established the fact that the phenomena produced by crystals to the sense of touch are accompanied by phenomena to the sense of vision, the latter phenomena following the former *pari passu*, in polar contrast of blue and red-yellow, and only perceptible by sensitives.

If you wish to make these experiments for yourself, I must warn you that you can only expect them to succeed in *absolute darkness*. The crystalline light is so fine and so extremely weak that if so much as a trace of any other light is perceptible anywhere in the dark chamber, it is sufficient to blind the sensitive observer, that is, to temporarily blunt his excitability of sense for so extremely weak a degree of light. Furthermore, there are but few human beings so highly sensitive to be able, like the young lady I have named, to perceive this delicate light after so short a period of darkness. For sensitives of a middling degree of power it has mostly taken one to two hours in the dark to sufficiently relieve their eyesight from the over-excitation of day- or lamp-light, and thus adequately to prepare it for the detection of the crystal-light. I have even had several cases in which weak sensitives gave no result after three hours, but who nevertheless succeeded quite well during the fourth hour in seeing crystals give out light and in convincing themselves of the reality of the phenomenon.

Now you are impatient to know what this really means, and where these phenomena fit in to physics and physiology, both as to their subjective and objective particulars. They are not heat, although they excite similar sensations to those of lukewarmness and coolness ; there is no conceivable source of heat in the case, and, were there any, it would be perceived, not only by sensitives, but also by non-sensitives, or in the ultimate issue by a fine thermoscope. They are not electricity ; for there is no excitation present to account for the eternally flowing stream, the electroscope is not affected, and conduction, in accordance with the laws of electricity, is without effect. It cannot be magnetism and diamagnetism, because crystals are not magnetic, and diamagnetism does not take effect in all crystals in the same sense, but in widely differing and contrasted senses—a matter that has no place here at all. It cannot be ordinary light, because, although light is here as an accompaniment, mere light never produces sensations of lukewarmness and coolness, etc. [See *Odische Begetenheiten* : Poggendorf's objection.]

Well, then, after saying all that, what *are* the phenomena you have described ? If you really wish to know, you compel me to admit that I do not know myself. I am becoming aware through sundry avenues of the presence of a natural force, for which I am unable to find a place on the record established by those forces we already know of. If my judgment of the facts I have been able to gather has not gone astray, this force fits in between electricity, magnetism, and heat, without being identifiable with any of the three ; so, in the embarrassment created by the occasion, I have provisionally designated it by the word " Od," the etymology of which I shall discuss later.

III

Sun—Moon—Rainbow

Sensitives you now know, and the element in which they move you know, namely, that force of nature which I have designated by the word "Od." But with all that we have only lifted one corner of the hem of the great odic garment in which the universe has wrapped itself. That remarkable force of od streams not only from the poles of the crystal, but gushes also from numerous other sources in the great world of being just as strongly, and even more strongly still.

First and foremost I shall take you to the stars, and, in fact, to the sun itself. Post a sensitive person in the shade, give him an ordinary unfilled barometer-tube, or any other sort of glass rod, or even a wooden stick, in his left hand, and let him hold the rod in the sunshine, while his person and hand remain in the shade. You will shortly learn something from this simple experiment that will surprise you. You naturally expect that the person experimenting will perhaps feel the rod getting warm ; the most that can happen will surely be that the sunshine will warm it up.

But you will hear exactly the opposite : the sensitive's hand will feel a number of effects, but the sum-total of them all will be—a coolness. If such a hand withdraw the rod into the shade, the coolness will vanish, and the hand will feel the rod getting warm ; if it put the rod back into the sunshine, the rod will once more grow cool to its sensory perception ; it can check the correctness of its own sensations by continuing to change about from one position to the other.

There are consequently some very simple, but so far unobserved, factors in existence under the influence of which the direct sunbeam not only does not warm, but, in a most unexpected and unusual manner, cools. And as to this coolness, sensitives will tell you that it bears every resemblance in its effects to those exercised by the coolness felt from the upper peak of the mountain-crystal.

Now, if this coolness is something in the nature of od, it will necessarily find some expression in the dark as a phenomenon of light. You will succeed in finding this out if you will perform one of my experiments as follows : I hung a copper wire so as to go from a fully lighted room into the darkness of the *camera obscura*. Then I put the end of the wire out into the sunshine. Scarcely was this done when the part of the wire that was in the dark began to get luminous, and a small, flame-like phenomenon, the size of a finger, rose up at its extremity. The sunshine consequently infused an odic element into the wire, seen by sensitives streaming out in the darkness under the form of light.

But take one step further ; let the sunbeam fall on a good glass prism, and throw the colours of the rainbow on to the nearest wall. Let the sensitive person with the glass rod in his left hand try the colours one after the other. If he hold it so as to catch only the blue or violet colour in the air, the sensation that this will excite in him will be one of a highly agreeable coolness, much purer and cooler than that which occurred with the unrefracted sunbeam. If, instead of this, he puts the rod into the yellow ray, or, better still, into the red ray, the comfortable feeling of coolness will vanish on the instant, and be replaced by one of heat ; a disagreeable lukewarmness will make his whole arm heavy.

You can make the sensitive hold a bare finger on the colours, instead of using the rod as intermediary ; the effect will be the same ; I only devised the rod for the purpose of shutting off the actual heat rays from his hand by means of a bad conductor of heat. These effects of refracted sunlight will be found exactly similar to those of the poles of the crystal. Hence you see : od exercising both kinds of effect is contained in the sunbeam ; it streams towards us from our star of day every moment in immeasurable floods, along with the light and heat, and forms a newly discovered mighty solar agent, the extent of whose functions we have no present means of estimating.

Will you now let me ask you to look back for a moment to the foe to yellow and friend to blue I spoke of in my first letter ? Have we not seen that the pole of the crystal that breathed forth an agreeable coolness was one that emitted blue light ? And do we not here, by quite a different route, come upon sunlight distributing with its blue ray an extremely agreeable and refreshing coolness ? And, vice versa, had not the red-yellow light of the other pole of the crystal, and also the red-yellow ray of the sun, produced feelings of nausea and discomfort in the sensitives ? You see how in two cases, standing so infinitely wide apart, blue had invariably for its sequel sensations of comfort, and red-yellow feelings of discomfort. Herewith you receive a preliminary hint to put you on your guard against all rash judgment of sensitive persons in the matter of their alleged whims. You see that, in fact, something more must lie hidden in the yellow and blue of our colours than their mere optical effect on the retina of the eye, that here a deep-down, instinctive sense of a subtle, unknown *something* guides the feeling and intuitive judgment of our sensitives, and that this is a matter worth the utmost efforts of our powers of observation.

Now, leaving colours on one side, I wish to arm you with one more easy experiment that I have often made for isolating the odic content of sunbeams. Polarize them in the ordinary way, so that they fall at an angle of 35° on a bundle of a dozen panes of glass. Then let the sensitive observer hold the rod in his left hand now in the reflected light and now in the light that has passed through. You will always hear that the former sends odic cool and the latter odic mawkishness along the rod to the sense of feeling in the hand.

If you are in the mood, you can take a little rise out of the chemists in this connection. Get two similar glasses of water and put one standing in the reflected and the other in the filtered sunlight. After they have been there six to eight minutes, let a sensitive sip from them. He will tell you at once that the water taken out of the reflected light tastes cool and slightly acidulous, and that the water taken out of the filtered light tastes mawkish and somewhat bitter. Do something more : put a small glass vessel filled with water in the blue light of the spectrum, and another one in the orange ; or put one of them at the pointed end of a large mountain-crystal, and the other at the butt-end. In all these cases you may be sure that the sensitive will find the water that has been in the blue light pleasant, and lightly acidulated, and that which has been in the orange nauseating, rather bitter, and crude. He will drink the first glass off with pleasure, if you let him do so ; but, if you force him into drinking the other, an event may betide you that happened once to myself, namely, that the sensitive shortly afterwards had a violent fit of vomiting. Now give the water to the gentlemen of the analytical profession, and ask them to try out the elements of the " amarum " and the " acidum " from it.

Proceed with the moonlight as you have done with the sunlight. You will obtain similar, but in part polarically contrasted results. A glass rod held by a sensitive's left hand in full, pure moonlight will not yield him coolness, but lukewarmness. A glass of water that has been some time in the moonlight he will find tasting more insipid and mawkish than another that has been standing a moderate time in the shade. Everyone knows the great influence the moon has on many people ; all persons subject to its influence are without exception sensitives, and as a rule pretty keenly sensitive. And, as the moon demonstrably exercises odic effects, while its influence on lunatic patients corresponds exactly with the effects that can be produced through other odic sources, it is as an od-distributive star of great importance for us.

The element of odic force is thus radiated towards us so abundantly by sunlight and moonlight that we can lay hold of it at our ease and make use of it in simple experiments. How unbounded its influence is on the whole of humanity, and even on the whole animal and vegetable kingdom, will be proved shortly. Od is, accordingly, a cosmic force that radiates from star to star, and has the whole universe for its field, just like light and heat.

IV

MAGNETISM

I HAVE headed these letters of mine Odic-Magnetic Letters. But why magnetic? What has magnetism got to do with them? you ask. My answer must almost be, " Little or nothing at all." But it has pleased the world to call a number of the phenomena which come in here magnetic, and I have to accommodate myself to the nomenclature demanded by the fashion of the day. The occasion for my doing so lies in the circumstance that magnetism has for its collaterals certain odic forces, just as sunlight and moonlight have a retinue of them, just as they proceed from the poles of a crystal, and just as they flow from numerous sources that have nothing even remotely in common with magnetism as we have so far understood it. Let us take a glance at the mutual relations of magnetism and od.

Lay a good rod-magnet transversely across the corner of a table, so that both ends project, as you did with the large crystal. Get the table into such a position that the rod will be left lying along the meridian, like the needle of a compass, with the northward pole to the north and the southward pole to the south. Now bring in a sensitive, and get him to gradually approach first one pole, then the other, to a distance of four or five inches, with the palm of his left hand. By this proceeding you will get the same declarations from him that he made in the case of the crystals, namely, that one of the poles, in this case the one turned towards the north, sends a cool breath of air to his hand, and that the

24

other turned towards the south gives out a lukewarm, mawkish breath.

Again, you can set a glass of water at each pole of the magnet, and after six or eight minutes get the sensitive to taste them. He will pronounce the glass at the pole turned to the north fresh and cool, and that at the pole turned towards the south lukewarm and disgusting ; and, if you wish to challenge our chemists again, they will get angry and, to free themselves from their embarrassment, will bluntly contest the observation made, though it be as clear as day, and tell you that it is not the fact. It is for you to smile at the simplicity evinced now and again *ex cathedra*—as if a truth of nature could be turned into an untruth by unsupported contradiction. In spite of themselves these gentlemen will have to think out some better answer before long.

You will naturally assume that the conjectures which took me into the dark with the crystals must have risen up to my mind for the case of magnets as well. I made my first experiment of this sort with Miss Mary Nowotny in Vienna during April 1844, and repeated it with other sensitives in the dark chamber a hundred times after. It was with satisfaction and delight that I ascertained my conjectures to have been justified, for she straightway stated that at both ends of the magnet-rod a flame was burning, luminous and fiery, smoking and sending out sparks, at the end to the north blue, at the end to the south yellow-red. But make the easy experiment yourself, and then vary it. Set the rod-magnet up on end, with its southward pole uppermost, and you will be told that the luminous body increases, mounting almost to the roof of the chamber if the magnet is strong enough. Indeed it will go so far as to produce an illuminated spot of a somewhat rounded shape on the ceiling itself, one, two or as many as three feet in diameter, and so bright that, if the sensitive is sufficiently responsive to excitation, he will be able to describe the decoration he sees there.

But I warn you not to omit any of the precautionary measures I have prescribed as to *absolute* darkness and preparation of the eyesight in darkness for hours at a time. If you omit one, your assistant in the experiment will see nothing ; you are labouring in vain ; and the exactness of my statements is exposed to undeserved suspicion.

A more beautiful appearance still will be presented by the luminous phenomenon, if a horseshoe magnet be used, set vertically with both poles upwards. I have in my possession a nine-layered horseshoe magnet with a lifting power of 100 lbs.; from each pole of this instrument all sensitives see a body of fine light—that is, two lights, one beside the other— streaming out ; they do not attract, do not coun- teract, do not influence each other as the magnetic forces of the two poles do, but quietly stream up on high, one beside the other ; they swarm with in- numerable little points of white light, and together form a column of light the size of a man's body, which everyone who saw it described as strikingly beautiful. It goes up vertically to the ceiling and there forms an illuminated round superficies of almost two yards diameter. If the spectacle is kept in view for a good time, the whole roof of the chamber becomes gradually visible.

If a magnet such as described stand upon a table, the flaming emanation lights up the surface of the latter and any ornaments set upon it for ells around. If a hand be interposed, a shadow is visibly thrown.

If any flat object, such as a bracket, a pane of glass, or a sheet of metal, is held horizontally in the flame-like phenomenon, the latter takes a bend round it and streams away from it underneath, just as the flame of any other fire acts when a pan or saucepan is brought into it. If you blow or breathe on it, it flickers just like the flame of a candle would do. If a draught is set up, or if one carries the magnet about, the flame goes on one side in the direction taken by the current of air, like the flame of a torch in motion. If a burning-glass be put to it, it admits of its light being gathered and condensed at the focus. The phenomenon is consequently quite a material one, and has many qualities in common with ordinary flame.

When two magnet-flames of the kind are brought together, so as to cross each other's path, they do not disturb each other by attractions or repulsions, but interpenetrate and keep without hindrance on their course. When one is stronger than the other, endowed apparently with a stronger power of projection, it penetrates the weaker, so that the latter is cloven and courses around it on both sides. The same takes place when a rod is held in it ; the rod splits the flame in two, and the flame reunites behind the rod. And just as the sensitives saw the crystals in a subtle body of light which penetrated their entire substance, so they now see the steel of the magnet fused through and through with a kind of whitish glow. Electro-magnets behave in just the same way.[1]

[1] For detailed treatment of these light-phenomena of magnets, with necessary proofs, see the treatise, *Researches in the Forces of Magnetism, Electricity, Heat, Light. etc., in their relations to Vital Force* (*Untersuchungen über die Dynamide des Magnetismus, der Elektricität, der Wärme, des Lichts, etc., in ihren Beziehungen zur Lebenskraft*), by Baron von Reichenbach. Vieweg 1850 ; Brunswick.

These qualities possess, as you will easily perceive, no parallelism with those of magnetism; they are characteristically odic. If you compare a crystal of gypsum spar with a rod-magnet, both as near as maybe of the same weight, you find no material difference between the odic emanations from the like poles, either in the effect upon the sensorium or in the matter of luminosity. In fact the crystal is even superior to the magnet in odic power; its cool and warmth is more distinct, and its strength of light greater. But a crystal has no magnetism. Here, then, you have a case of od associated *with* magnetism, and a case of od *without* magnetism, and in both cases you have od of *like* strength. It cannot consequently be in any way asserted that od is a connecting link with magnetism, or that it is only one of the qualities of magnetism, or that it is magnetism itself. Od is found in the crystal quite apart from magnetism, and I shall quote you quite a number of just as striking examples in which od presents itself in the highest degree of force, while any magnetism (in the ordinary sense) is far from being present.

Od must therefore be regarded as a force in itself, which shows itself in the train of magnetism, as it enters into the train of crystals, sunbeams, and many other natural phenomena which we shall touch upon. We know the great resemblance that exists between magnetism and electricity; we know that one appears so often as a sequel to the other, and vice versa, that we come near taking them to be identical. Light and heat are on the same footing; one calls the other forth, and every moment each is being transformed into the other; and, in spite of all that, we are unable to lay our finger anywhere on the common point of departure from which they both have their origin. So it is with od. We suspect, I grant you, that these dynamic phenomena emerge in the last instance from a common source ; but so long as we are not in a position to identify the unit which gives them their origin, so long nothing remains for us to do but to treat of electricity, magnetism, light, heat, and so on, as constituting, each one of them, a separate group of phenomena in itself.

In consequence of the fact that we find ourselves unable to list the numerous odic phenomena under any of the known natural forces, nothing remains for us but to bring them together and treat them as a special group. That they yield in no respect, either in range or importance, to those already enjoying civic rights in our schools of physics, my following letters will give you good reason to be convinced.

V

ANIMAL MAGNETISM

JUST now [1852] we are hearing a good deal more about the wonderful thing that more than 80 years ago Mesmer called Animal Magnetism. Our fathers, our grandfathers, and our great-grandfathers rejected it body and bones, and yet it is always coming up again and refusing to die. What can such tough vitality be based upon? On " lies and fraud and superstition ? " as one of our eminent Berlin physiologists declared—to find a short way of getting rid of it. . . . Well, we shall see if those have done well who could think of nothing better than to repeat the same sing-song.

This time let us take the subject by the horns at once without further preamble. Take a good middling or a good high-sensitive into the dark, and along with him a cat, a bird, a butterfly, if it is to be had, and a pot of flowers in bloom. After a couple of hours have gone by, you will hear strange stories. The flowers, so you will be told, will come forth out of the gloom and grow visible. First of all they will distinguish themselves from the black night of the general darkness in the form of a vaguely defined grey cloud. In this, later on, clearer spots will be formed. These will finally separate from each other definably ; the individual blooms will become distinguishable ; forms will become recognizable as they gradually grow clearer and clearer ; and, on one occasion, when I had left a flowerpot as I have described with the late Professor Endlicher, the celebrated botanist, who was a sensitive of

medium power, he cried out with a shock of astonishment : " It is a blue flower—it is a gloxinia ! "   It
was in fact a *gloxinia speciosa*, var. *coerulea*, which
he had seen in absolute darkness and recognized both
as to shape and colour.

Nothing can be seen in darkness without light.
Consequently, light must have been there for colour
as well as form to have been recognized.   And
whence came the light ?   It came from the plant
itself : the plant was luminous !   Calyx, pistils,
stamen, corolla, stem, everything showed out in a
fine light ; even the leaf could be seen, though more
dully.   Everything shone out in a delicate glow,
the genitals most clearly, the stem brighter than the
leaf.

Your butterfly, your bird, your cat—all will appear
in the darkness ; parts of them will become luminous
and move with the moving bodies to and fro.   But,
shortly, you will receive the declaration from the
sensitive that he sees—you yourself !   You will first
appear to him like an unshapely, white, snow-man,
then like a man in armour with a high helmet, finally
an object of terror as a luminous giant.

Direct the sensitive's gaze to his own person ;
he will be somewhat struck to perceive that he
himself is luminous ; not only his arms, but his feet,
his legs, his chest, his body through his clothes ;
he will see everything shimmering in a fine glow.

Direct his attention to his hands.   They will first
appear like a grey smoke, then like a silhouette on a
slightly illuminated background ; finally the fingers
will show out in their own light ; they will present
the appearance that they get when one holds one's
hand close to the flame of a candle, transparent as

it were. The hand will show out longer than it really is ; there will be a luminous prolongation to every finger, and from each finger-tip a body of light will stream out that, according to circumstances, will be half, or just, as long as the finger itself. Owing to these tails of fire on every finger the hand will seem to be twice its real length. The finger-tip phalanges will be the brightest, and of these the brightest parts will be at the roots of the nails.

When you have recovered from your first astonishment at this hitherto unrevealed self-luminosity of all mankind, and you think of putting a question about your colour, your astonishment will possibly be renewed when you hear that it is not the same in different parts of the body, that right hands are luminous with a bluish fire, while left hands appear a yellowish red, and that the latter are on that account brighter than the former ; that the same difference exists between the two feet ; that even the whole right side of your face is darker and more bluish than the left, and that, in fact, the whole right side of your entire body is bluish and somewhat darker than the other, while the whole left side comes out reddish-yellow and distinctly brighter.

It cannot fail to occur to you that here you encounter the same contrast of blue and red-yellow that met your attention in the light of the crystal, in sunshine, and in the flames of the magnet.

Will the parallelism found existent in all cases between cool and blue, and lukewarm and red-yellow—odlight—be found and proved existent also in the case of the human light ? That you hold for doubtful ; and yet, were such a fact not verifiable, the nature of the human light would remain a puzzle.

I experimented as follows, in August 1845, with a cabinet-maker named Bollmann, in Vienna, a medium-sensitive, 50 years of age :

I laid my right hand in his left, so that our fingers crossed, but scarcely touched. After a minute I replaced my right hand by my left fingers. I made these alternations a few times to and fro, and was informed by the sensitive that he felt my blue-lit right hand cooler than my yellow-lit left, which seemed to him much warmer.

What I had been in search of was found. I repeated the experiment exactly with more than a hundred other sensitives, and the same was verified in every instance. Then I extended the experiment to the feet, the sides of the body, the cheeks, the ears, the eyes, the nostrils, even the two sides of the tongue, with innumerable diversifications of the conditions ; but I invariably received one and the same result, namely, that to the sensitive's left hand the whole right side of every human being, whether male or female, was felt to be cooler, and the whole left side, on the contrary, warmer.

You thus see that man is polarized from right to left, in just the same way, and with the same characteristics, as a crystal between the poles of its chief axis, as the magnet between its north and south, and as the sunlight between blue and red-yellow. And, as the effects, with their characteristics, are the same, we have the right to argue back that the causes also will be the same, and it follows that man too emits od, and just in the same two forms as we have hitherto observed in all other odic sources. I have tested cats, chickens, ducks, dogs, horses, and oxen in the same way ; they were all found just the same. Plants, which I have investigated, from root to leaves, showed themselves subject to the same laws.

Thus everything, the whole nature of organic life, beams and abounds in a streaming wealth of odic force, and if you will only call up for review this great comprehensive fact in its boundless range throughout the created Universe, you will witness the dawn of a new day for that of which man has hitherto named a small portion, with as much impropriety as inadequacy, "animal magnetism." I shall take you on a cursory trial trip now, my theory in my hand, through this intricate territory : I have just handed you the key to its outer gate.

VI

MAN AS OD-CONTAINER

You have seen that, if I laid my right hand in the left of a sensitive, an agreeably cool feeling was aroused, but that, if I did the same with my left, a disagreeable warmth and sensation of nausea was the result. The procedure can be reversed : lay your own left hand in the sensitive's right, and he will experience a cool and agreeable sensation ; put your own right hand in his, and the disagreeable, lukewarm sensation will commence. This gives us a law : contact of hands odically like (left with left, or right with right) is disagreeably lukewarm ; contact of hands odically unlike (left with right) is agreeably cool.

Now, please, recall the remark I made in my first letter, to the effect that there were people who found it disagreeable to be given a man's hand, and who wrenched themselves free if the hand they extended was retained. According to common custom, men always give each other their right hands, and thus cause a contact of hands odically like ; such a contact is disagreeably lukewarm to sensitives, becomes quite penal, then speedily unendurable, and—they free themselves.

Go a step further : put the fingers of your right hand on the sensitive's left arm, on his shoulder, under his arm-pit, on his temples, on the small of his back, on his knee, his foot, his toes, everywhere on the left side of the sensitive's body, and he will feel them, your right fingers, cool and comfortable : the contacts are all odically unlike. Do the same to the sensitive's right side with the fingers of your left, and they will produce the same feelings of coolness : those are unlike contacts too. But do all these touches on the sensitive's left side with the fingers of your left hand, or on his right side with the fingers of your right, and it will all be found nauseating and, every touch, disagreeable : they are like contacts.

Put my data to the proof by another kind of pairing taken from common life. Stand as close to a sensitive as soldiers do when drawn up in rank and file ; the whole of your right side will then touch the whole of the sensitive's left : you will hear no complaint from him on the subject. But now make a right-about turn, so as to bring your left side into contact with the sensitive's left, and complaints will at once be forthcoming : he will have a sickening sense of discomfort, and if you do not turn round again soon, he will not keep on, but will take a step backwards. In the first instance an unlike, in the second a like, contact was at work.

Choose another condition. Post yourself close behind your sensitive, with your front to his rear ; or in the same way, in front of him, with your rear to his front. In both cases your right side is planted against the sensitive's right, and your left against his left. In both respects these are odically like pairings ; the sensitive cannot endure them, and if you do not speedily change the situation, he will change it for you by stepping to one side. Here again I must ask you to look up my first letter, at the place where I drew your attention to the fact that there were some people who could not bear others standing before them or behind them, and on that account avoided popular assemblies, crowds, and market-places. You see now what good grounds they had for their action.

I know strong and active young men who do not like riding. It seems something almost against human nature : to youthful vigour it is surely the height of enjoyment to be tossed up on horseback. But when one is in the saddle one has to present like sides to those of one's mount.   The case is thus exactly the same as having a man's back immediately in front of one. The men I found exhibiting this disinclination were all sensitives : I may mention as instances among them Barons August and Heinrich von Oberländer.

In the same way there are women who cannot give a child a ride on their back, not even for a few minutes for pure sport.   The case is almost the same as the foregoing ; it comes to the same as having someone close behind one ; women of this sort are always sensitives.

Many men are simply unable to sleep two in a bed ; *mauvais coucheurs*—bad bedfellows—are proverbial. The reason breaks in upon us after what we have discussed.

But the practice common to all civilized societies of presenting our right side to all privileged persons, by always standing to their left, sitting down at their left, taking their left arm, has its fundamental cause in our odic nature.   It is said, of course, that this is to leave the privileged person's right hand free. That may play its part in regard to the custom, but the influence of sensitivity must bear down the scale with still greater weight.   When two men sit side by side they set free their od mutually upon each other ; the man on the right gets a discharge of negative od from the man on the left, the man on the left positive od from the man on his right.   The right-hand-side man thus gains as much in negativity as the left-hand-side man loses, and the latter gains as much in positivity as the man on the right discharges. Now the condition of greater odic negativity, as we know, is the colder and more agreeable of the two, and that of greater positivity the warmer and more disagreeable. So when we place a lady on our right, she acquires just as much comfort as the man on her left takes upon himself in the way of discomfort. The key to this ancient custom, therefore, is not to be found entirely in tradition, but rather in the innermost depth of human nature. The matter goes so far, that people who are at all strong sensitives are unable to retain a position on the left for any length of time.

Cases such as I have mentioned are innumerable in human life, and occur in thousands of connections and varieties of circumstance; they may all be accounted for and judged by the law we have just made out. And it will be recognized too what good grounds sensitives often have for their claims to consideration and forbearance.

VII

MESMERISM—THE MESMERIC PASS AND THE DOCTORS

YOU will now ask me what, from the point of view arrived at, the so-called magnetizing of a man consists in, and you will perhaps regard this as the pivot upon which my letters hinge. Well, that is not at all the case ; but still it is a very noteworthy side of the odic phenomena. It has won for itself a position of great practical importance, and leads up to what is called Mesmerism, that is, the method introduced in medical practice by Dr. Mesmer of using the odic dynamid in the treatment of disease. Mesmer took it for magnetism, swayed by the condition of natural science in his time, and called it " Animal Magnetism." The two expressions, od and mesmerism, need not stand in each other's way : the former term is proper to natural science, and designates a force permeating all Nature, the latter stands for a special application of this force to therapy, and is proper to the art of healing.

Here let us link up with Letter v. of this series, in which I invited you to accompany me, with the light of my new-won theory in hand, on a rapid excursion through the intricate territory of this so-called animal magnetism.

You know that, whenever you touch a sensitive with your fingers, you exercise an effect upon him which he can feel and, when in darkness, see. But it is not even necessary to come into actual contact with him ; the mere approach of your fingers produces effects that are considerable. The emanation, which darkness discloses to be streaming from the fingers to points beyond, inevitably reaches the body to which the fingers are brought near, and takes effect upon it. You can produce very strong excitations at a distance of several inches ; but by sensitives of a middling degree of sensitivity you will be felt a foot off, or even at a distance of several feet. And in the case of high-sensitives the effect goes far beyond that—to the end of the room ; in fact, I have had several cases in which the effect made itself clearly perceptible at the astonishing distance of twenty and thirty paces and more.

So far we have only considered contact when at rest, pairings without motion. But now I invite you to make a forward movement with your finger-tips, or the flat of your hand, or the pole of a crystal, or with a magnet, from any one place on the sensitive's body to any other. Place your right finger-tips, for instance, on your sensitive's left shoulder, and draw them gently and gradually down as far as his elbow joint, or, if you like, down his whole arm to the fingers and beyond. As you formerly did by your stationary contacts, so now by your contact in motion you will produce an effect downwards along the whole line ; you will produce a cool stroking, which can be regarded as a chain of innumerable points of coolness produced. This is what the physicians call a " pass."

Do the same on other parts, over the left side of the head, the left of the body, the left foot to the toes and beyond ; you will leave a sensation of coolness behind along the line taken. Perform the same movements with your left hand down the subject's right side, and you will produce the same effects as before : both are unlike pairings.

Finally, take both your hands together and draw both the prescribed passes, right and left, over the sensitive's whole body, from the crown of his head to the toes on his feet ; the whole man so stroked, will be conscious of an agreeable sense of coolness and repose stealing over his entire person. What you have now done is what Mesmer's disciples and all the so-called magnetic doctors term an animal-magnetic or mesmeric pass. You are now able to magnetize.

It is more or less a matter of indifference in the case, as you will easily see, whether you make the pass with your hands, the poles of a crystal, or with magnets, whether you do it directly on the bare skin or over the clothing, at a distance of half a span, or an ell, or more ; a like effect in kind will always be produced, only falling off in strength as the distance is increased.

It is thus the influence of alien, unlike emanations of od on the part of a sensitive which constitutes the essence of this so-called magnetizing. When done in darkness, sensitives see the fiery bundles of the stroking fingers, or poles, drawn down over them ; they see, furthermore, just where the flames stream against them, a spot on their own body developing a stronger volume of light, which courses over them beneath the luminous excitant.

From this luminous phenomenon, as well as from the sense of coolness produced, you clearly recognize the fact that the person making the passes causes an excitation to the organism of the person over whom the passes are made, and an excitation that must be called an important one ; for the od radiating blue light effects, in a way altogether peculiar to itself, an excitation upon the subject of the od with red light, unlike working unlike. And as the human body is a receptacle strongly charged with od, while the odic matter is powerfully connected with its inmost depths, the fact of odic passes being able to penetrate deeply into the physical and mental economy of the subject is intelligible. The production of sleep or restlessness, beneficent or deleterious influences upon morbid disturbances in the body, and effects produced by " the laying on of hands, stroking, and the like " are consequently no " deplorable aberration of deceit and fraud and superstition," as persons in certain quarters think themselves justified in maintaining, but are physiological facts quite in accord with natural laws and well founded in experience. Only such as have never cared to take the trouble to test the facts can allow such premature judgments to escape them in the matter.

If you ask me what actual profit the healing art derives from the odic pass treatment, I do, it is true, entertain the conviction that it is capable of *becoming* unboundedly great, when physics as a science and odic physiology are adequately developed, but I do not shrink from confessing, that, so far, it seems to me of a very limited and uncertain nature. To hear and read what the magnetizers have to say, they are, I admit, as Mesmer claimed eighty years ago, in the position of being able to-day to cure nearly all diseases. Every physician, to whatever school he belongs, imagines when a patient recovers that it is he and his art that have cured the sufferer. Why, then, should the magnetizing practitioner indulge in any less degree of self-satisfaction ?

We who do not belong to the medical profession know well enough that of every twenty patients who attain convalescence nineteen get on to their legs again of themselves, and in some cases in spite of the doctors. But apart from all that, I have in general found it to be a certain fact that at every spot of the human body on which a hand was laid or moved in unlike odic pairing, a rise in vitality took place, and not a mere superficial rise, but one which penetrated deeply into the internal organs. Consequently in cases of local debility a vitalizing and enhancement of activity can be induced. That is a great and comprehensive general result which far-seeing medical practitioners will appreciate. Then, in special, I regard the influence of od upon cramp as decided ; I have on innumerable occasions relieved cramp and induced it at will. But when I have seen physicians operating beside the sick-bed, I have observed them, with few exceptions, cutting such capers in opposition to all sound odic science, that it was impossible that any benefit could result therefrom to the patients. Without any knowledge of the nature and laws of so complicated a force as od, how could any solid good be attained by contrectations performed almost at random ?

But let us hope that, if the nature of od and its complex relations with the forces of the living organism come to be recognized and scientifically made known by systematic research, our doctors too will begin to substitute a rational procedure for the fumbling in the dark that has hitherto prevailed, to record under fixed laws the effective working of od upon the patient's body, and to derive a reliable remedy from these extraordinary things to the advantage of the world, which has long justly expected it.

VIII

CHEMICAL REACTION

I HAVE just shown you what is understood by animal magnetism : it is not a magnetic effect, but an odic effect, upon the human body, which is exercised by countless other odic subjects just as well as, and sometimes much better than, by means of the magnet, which only, indeed, comes into play at all contingently, as an od-container, and not as a magnet proper. We consequently set aside the inappropriate word " animal magnetism " as something obsolete. It comes down from a time when the obscurest and most confused ideas were conceived about these matters, and can no longer be tolerated under present conditions of theoretic enlightenment on the subject. Before, however, I guide you further in this respect into the subject's depths, I must, as a preliminary, make you still further acquainted with the range of od throughout Nature.

You know of od which, from causes unknown, flows ceaselessly and unchangeably from the poles of the crystal. You know it as it proceeds from a gradually weakening and vanishing source, the steel magnet. Finally you know it as it gushes from a transitory but living fount, the being endowed with organic life. I wish to guide you to it now as it momentarily flames forth, to be speedily again extinguished, in virtue of a chemical process, that is to say of a chemical *reaction*, to be definitely distinguished here from *affinity*, which is the term designating chemical force.

While in the dark along with your sensitive, open a bottle of champagne. He will be pleasantly astonished to mark the apparition of a trail of fire following the flight of the cork from the neck of the bottle to the ceiling. The whole bottle will show up a brilliant white, as if made of luminous snow, and above it will play a cloud, waving lightly from side to side. As you yourself see nothing of all the fine pyrotechnic display, you know at once that it is an odic phenomenon. If you wish to understand its nature, experiment with me a little further.

Still in the dark, throw a spoonful of finely granulated sugar, or smoothly crushed table salt into a glass of water. Before you did so, your sensitive saw little, perhaps nothing, of either one or the other substance ; but, as soon as you stir them round in the water together, he will see both water and glass become luminous on the instant. If he holds the glass in his left hand, he will feel it getting very cold. Simple *solution* (Lösung), therefore, with nothing further, is a developer of od : it is an odic source.

Put an iron, copper, or zinc wire into a glass vessel containing diluted sulphuric acid. The whole wire will get into a glow, as it were, and a luminous apparition will emerge from its upper end, in form pretty well resembling the flame of an ordinary candle, only immeasurably weaker in illuminating power. At the summit this will resolve itself into smoke, with a great number of fine sparks, streaming vertically upwards. To the sensitive's left hand the wire will feel much colder than it was before. *Dissolution* (Auflösung) therefore is also a source of od.

Make up a saline draught with effervescing powder. First of all, while you are in the dark, dissolve the bicarbonate of soda in half a glass of water ; it will at once become luminous. Then dissolve the tartaric acid in another half-glassful of water ; it too will become luminous, and more so than the other. Wait a few minutes till they have become dark again, and then pour the solutions together. In an instant the mixture will become brilliantly luminous, seem icy cold to the left hand, and a mighty cloud of white light will tower upwards over the glass. Chemical *decomposition* (Zerlegung) therefore is a vigorous developer of od in abundance.

Make a solution of sugar of lead, and pour in a solution of alum : on the instant the whole liquid will appear visible in the dark. Conduct the wires from the two poles of a voltaic battery into the water ; as soon as decomposition sets in, your sensitive will see the water luminous and getting brighter and brighter, and feel the vessel containing it cold to his left hand.

All chemical activity consequently develops od ; chemical reaction is an odic source which comes vigorously and suddenly into play, but which ceases on the spot so soon as the interaction of the affinities comes to an end.

If you take the stopper from a bottle of alcohol, or, better still, ether, bisulphide of carbon, or caustic ammonia, but best of all, pure eupion of 0.65 specific gravity, when in the dark and the air kept free from draughts, a sensitive person sees a column of light ascending vertically from the opening, with a velocity directly proportional to the tension of the substance. While this is going on, the liquid in the container becomes luminous. And not only substances so highly volatile as those named, but other bodies also, such as quicksilver, with its extremely low degree of evaporating power, emit a luminous vapour from the neck of the bottle. Solids such as camphor behave in the same way, and in particular iodine, which not only emits a brightly luminous vapour, but becomes luminous at the same time itself. *Evaporation* and *steaming*, therefore, and consequently *distillation*, take place with a constant development of od.

All fermenting, sugar-laden liquids give a continuous display of luminosity ; their bubbles mount to the surface like glowing pearls. Fermenting wine-must is one of these chemically active liquids that keep up a constant condition of luminosity. The bursting of your champagne into fire and flames you can now account for without any help from me. Putrefaction also is a process of fermentation, and for this reason all putrefying matter becomes luminous. That, of course, is a fact that has been known to us all for a long time from the science of phosphorescence ; but how closely connected it is with the odic light we have not yet discussed ; in instances in which we non-sensitives cannot perceive a trace of phosphorescence in putrefying matter, such matter is shown up to sensitives in full luminosity.

And as we are now touching on the subject of corruption, we find ourselves not far removed from the idea of the departed. Follow me for a moment into the realms of death, and you may rely upon my word that I shall guide you speedily back again, all the wiser for an instructive glimpse at the doings of the night. You are aware, I fancy, that the souls of the departed linger about their graves for a time in flames of fire, till they have purged and atoned for the earthly dross clinging to them from this side of the tomb and have acquired eternal rest ? You are giving me a doubtful look ? But I am quite in earnest ; such ghosts are really seen ; you have the evidence of sufficient witnesses on the point.

Your nurse, too, is pretty sure to have told you that it is not given to everyone to see the ghosts or souls of the departed, but that only certain persons are privileged to be witnesses of the apparition. All this came home to me with full effect when I was working with some good sensitives on the subject of fish-putrescence, and wanted to see whether I could not make the acquaintance of the dead in their flames of fire. Miss Leopoldina Reichel consented to be taken one very dark night to the cemetery of Grünzing, near Vienna, no great distance from my own house. And as a matter of fact she saw (November, 1844) fiery phenomena on several of the graves.

Taken on a later occasion to the huge burial-grounds of Vienna, she saw a number of the burial mounds beset by moving lights. They moved in uniformity to and fro, almost like rows of dancers, or soldiers at drill. Some were large, almost the size of men, and others small, creeping on the ground like dwarfish kobolds. But they were only to be seen among the more recent grave-rows ; the old burial-mounds had no fiery guard on duty. Miss Reichel went timidly and slowly up to them. As she approached, the human-like figures melted away ; she recognized the fact that they were no more than luminous clouds, such as she had seen in my dark chamber a thousand times. She now had the courage to go up to them, but only encountered a shining vapour ; she walked without fear right into one of them ; it reached as high as her neck, and she was able to whisk it about with movements of her skirt. The dancing and drilling was explained by movements of the wind, which had played the same game with all the luminosities simultaneously.

Another time I commissioned four sensitive persons to go to the cemetery at Sievring. It was so dark that some of them fell down repeatedly on their way there, but when they got up to the graves, they all saw the fiery, ghost-like figures, more or less clearly according to their different grades of sensitive excitability. A luminous atmosphere, they said, seemed to hang over the newly made graves. One lady in the company drew figures with the point of her umbrella on one of the graves ; the lines she drew remained there permanently, in a still stronger luminosity, over the scratches she made in the soil.

Well, what was that ? Or, what is that ? It is nothing else than the miasma of putrefaction breathed forth from the graves and mounting upwards in the air above them, where the wind plays upon them, and human terror pictures their movements to and fro in the wind as the dances of living ghosts. It is carbonate of ammonium, phosphoretted hydrogen [PH_3, $P_4 H_2$, $P_4 H_2$], and other products of putrefaction, known and unknown, which liberate odic light in the process of evaporation. When the putrefaction comes to an end, the lights are quenched —the dead have atoned.

But, dear reader, we ourselves have atonement to make—to our " old wives." We must entreat their pardon for the injustice we have done them in the matter of their " tales." Their fiery ghosts seen over graves exist in actuality and truth ; such a reality can never be denied ; we must give in to our " old wives " on the subject, for they are in the right. Yes, even down to the fact that the ghosts cannot be seen by everyone, but only by chosen mortals—i.e. the sensitives ; we must, to our confusion, admit even that point. It is not the " old wives' " fault that we have taken so long to understand what they assured us of thousands of years ago.

IX

Sound—Friction—The Sources

In my last letter we made an attack upon superstition, hunting it down to a hiding-hole it had lurked in for centuries. To-day I wish to deal it another blow of the same kind. Let us pursue the part played by od in the scheme of the universe still further.

In October 1851 I had taken a Viennese artisan, Mr. Enter, a sensitive of medium power, into the dark chamber, with the idea of finding out whether **Sound** stood in any connection with od or not. I took an air-pump bell by the button, and struck it cautiously with a key. As soon as it sounded, it became luminous and visible. The stronger the stroke the clearer the light. A metal rod and a horseshoe magnet increased in luminosity as they resounded to percussion. A bell made of metal, which had a powerful, penetrating tone, became so luminous after being rung continuously for some little time, that a clear light, visible to all sensitives, was diffused throughout the entire room. When a violin was played, not only its strings but the whole sounding-board became luminous.

The bodies thus emitting sound became not only themselves refulgent with odic light, but also created an area of luminous clearness round about them ; they were beset by a holy aureola (*Heiligenschein*). Every drinking-glass that I struck with a knife, as is commonly done by diners to catch the waiter's attention, acquired its environment of light, brighter in proportion to the height of the tone yielded in the musical scale. The luminosity could be seen to quiver in sympathy with the sound. And in each case it was precisely the spot on which the stroke fell that was the brightest.

I made the sensitives hold their hands inside these glass and metal bells, taking care not to establish contact at any point with the body of the instrument. When I now struck the latter on the outside, and the tone rang out, the sensitive's left hand was excited to a sensation of coolness and his right to one of luke-warmness. Odic effect upon the sense of touch consequently entered in here as a factor, just as it did in the case of the blue sunbeam, the upper peak of the crystal, and the northward pole of the magnet. In a word, I had the satisfaction of discovering a new and very strong source of od in Sound.

On another occasion I turned my attention to **Friction,** and in July, 1844, placed a copper wire, to the other end of which I had fixed a small plate, in the left hand of Miss Maria Maix. When I rubbed the plate with another one similar to it, a current of heat went through the long wire to the hand of the sensitive. When I experimented in the dark, and subjected the wire itself to friction from the wheel of a lathe, the whole wire showed the odic glow: it became enveloped in luminosity throughout its length, and a light shaped like the flame of a candle rose from the extremity farthest from the friction.

With a view to checking this result, I took a glass barometer-tube, and put one end of it in a glass of water. I then submitted the other end to a few minutes' friction from the rapidly revolving stone of the lathe. The whole tube, together with the glass of water, became luminous. All the sensitives who tasted it found it warm, rather bitter, and mawkish, and one lady among them, whom I persuaded to drink the entire contents of the glass, had violent and repeated fits of vomiting shortly afterwards. A very active development of od from friction as a source was thus set beyond a doubt.

The application of this knowledge led to a result which I expect you will be glad to know about. I wanted to find out whether the **friction of liquids** also gave evidence of the presence of od, and found that closed glass vessels containing alcohol, ether, acetone, oil of turpentine, and creosote, all became luminous in the dark, together with their contents, when shaken. Even water shaken in stoppered bottles became luminous, and to the left hand unpleasantly tepefied. As soon as the water was once more at rest, it became in a few seconds invisible and on the way to regaining its cooling quality.

Something uncommon now occurred to me. Do not be alarmed, dear reader ; but it was nothing more nor less than—the divining-rod, with all its evil repute ! The water-dowser,[1] the spring-finder, came up to my memory ! Ha ! said I to myself, if water sets od in motion when shaken, why should not running water perhaps do the same ?

To put the matter to the proof, I wrapped a glass tube thickly round with paper and placed it in this condition in the left hand of my sensitives. I then contrived a continuous flow of water down the tube through a glass funnel leading from glass tanks that

[1] Wassersucher, lit. "water-seeker." Our word "dowser" is, I think, Gaelic "damhsoir," so pronounced, and meaning "dancer," the traditional dance of the Gaels involving a plucking away of the feet uneasily upwards from the earth. Murray's great dictionary (see under "Dowser"), which takes but little account of Keltic lore, fails to find a certain derivation for this word, which seems, however, to give an unexpected support to the Reichenbach theory, if my suggestion as to its etymology be well founded.

stood on a higher level. The sensitives all found that warmth came to them through the paper as long as I kept pouring, and that coolness returned whenever I left off. When I made the experiment in the dark, the water became luminous in the funnel during the act of pouring in, and immediately afterwards the whole length of the tube became luminous also as the water flowed down it. There was no doubt about it ; water was developing od by merely running through a tube. My hopes increased.

I now took Miss Zinkel, a medium sensitive, out into the park round my country house. I knew the direction of a watercourse that runs under a great meadow in the forest there without being noticeable on the surface. I got her to walk slowly across the meadow, so that she would have to pass over the watercourse. When she got near it, I saw her stand stock still, then walk backwards and forwards, and finally come to a stop. At this point, she assured me, she had a feeling of disagreeable tepidity as far up as her knees, and particularly in her left foot, a thing that had not been the case in any other part of the entire meadow. She was, in fact, standing exactly over the pipe that brought water to the farm from a source half an hour's walk distant.

I repeated this experiment with numerous other sensitives, and always with the like result. There you see the dowsing-rod rise superior to the deep contempt into which it had been plunged by ignorance and undeserved ridicule ! Not to be sure the rod as such— that, likely enough, is only a cloak with which the truth has been enveloped—but all the more certain is the inner kernel of the truth that lay concealed, unable to obtain recognition. There then ! The effect is nothing else than that of od released by aqueous friction, whose movements are felt by sensitives.

Monsieur Sourcier, the celebrated water-dowser in France, whom people send for from long distances in the country, and who has brought water-finding to a wonderful pitch of perfection, is surely nothing else than a good sensitive ; as soon as he steps over any subterranean water in motion, he feels its odic effect on his susceptible body. From the greater or lesser excitation he is sensible of he can infer the greater or lesser depth of the water and, through practice, he has brought the thing to a perfection and certainty that has won for him the admiration and gratitude of half the French nation. His secret, which was an unanswerable riddle to himself, has now been divulged, and perhaps we shall soon have in Germany hundreds of men and women dowsers ; with a little practice all high-sensitives will become adepts at the art. And the divining-rod is from this time forth revealed as the common possession of the entire world.

X

HEAT—ELECTRICITY—THE WORLD OF MATTER

No action on my part is necessary to direct your attention to the part which such mighty agencies as heat and electricity must surely play in respect of od. But the matter grows so very complicated at this point that I see no room for it within the narrow confines of a few letters, and must restrict myself to a few short, comprehensive facts.

Present a brazier of glowing charcoal to a high-sensitive, or burn spirits of wine in his vicinity, or set him at a few paces' distant from a wood fire, or throw a few granules of potassium into water in his presence, and question him as to the sensation all this causes him. You will surely expect that he will answer, " Heat." You and your sensitive, however, will be struck at having to hear and feel respectively that it is not warmth, but coolness, that is his predominant sensation through all these fireworks.

Give him a light, wooden rod about an ell in length ; let him take hold of it by one end in his left hand, and set fire to it at the other ; he will find that coolness is produced in his hand as long as the rod burns. Give him an iron or glass rod instead, or a porcelain tube, and let him heat it over the chimney of a lamp with an Argand burner ; he will tell you with a shake of the head in each case that the rod is getting cold.

The explanation of this anomaly in the law of heat is that heating, just like the action of burning, develops od.

55

Hang a metal wire about the thickness of a straw in the dark chamber, so that part of it is inside and another part outside, say, let through the door. Put the outside portion on to a chafing-dish and heat it up. As soon as the calefaction begins outside, your sensitive in the dark will report the apparition of a small, luminous flame at his extremity of the wire.

I do not wish to call a halt here, but to hurry on at once to the subject of electricity, only to dispose of it, however, by sketching a few of its traits. The prevailing sensation reported by all sensitives when taken into the neighbourhood of any object of a good size charged with positive electricity, is coolness. But an electrophore yields lukewarmness, while the fur used with it emits coolness.[1]

When with your sensitive in the dark, strike a cake of resin very smartly with a fox's brush, and let him look at it sideways. You will hear him say that he sees a flame-like, lambent body of light rise up from the cake, something like a foot and a half in

---

[1] The electrophorus or electrophore [Greek for "electricity-carrier"] is an instrument for obtaining statical [i.e. "standing," "constant," "stored up"] electricity by means of induction, and consists of a round cake of resin, which is negatively electrified by being struck or rubbed with a catskin on flannel. A polished metal disk, fitted with an insulating handle attached at right angles to its centre, may now be set flat upon the cake. "Under these circumstances the upper plate does not receive a direct charge from the lower, but is positively charged on the lower surface and negatively on the upper; if now the [metal] disk is touched by the finger, the negative electricity passes to the ground, leaving the [metal] disk charged positively. On being lifted away by its insulating handle, it [i.e. the metal disk] is found to be charged, and will give a spark. It may then be replaced on the lower plate [i.e. the resin cake], and the process repeated an indefinite number of times, if the weather is favourable. The electricity obtained each time is the equivalent of the mechanical work done in separating the two surfaces against the attraction of the unlike electricities."—*Century Dictionary and Encyclopædia.* We owe the electrophore to Volta.

height. The brush will look like a roller of white light. After a few minutes the flame from the cake will die out ; but, while blazing, it will emit a luminous smoke rising as far as the ceiling, where it traces a great area of illumination, such as you already know of in the case of crystals and the poles of the magnet.

I have a good-sized electrical machine planted with its pedestal on the floor of my room, and its conductor in the same way, the whole making up an apparatus of considerable size. When the machine is at rest, medium-sensitives see practically nothing of it in the dark. If the glass disk is set in motion, so slowly that no electrical light is visible anywhere, the whole apparatus nevertheless becomes luminous with a white light. Some sensitives drew a peculiar comparison between it and a cart laden with lime, which they described as presenting the same sort of whiteness to the look.

A Leyden jar, when charged with electricity, became luminous through and through. A long iron wire which I ran through the dark chamber, with both ends outside, by means of which I kept discharging the jar from without, glowed white throughout its length at every discharge, for a period of from four to five minutes. At the moment of each discharge, the sensitives saw an unusually bright spark flash along the wire with the speed of lightning, from which they were able to give me the exact direction taken by the discharges, that is to say, from the inner lining to the outer.

As to the voltaic column, I will only mention the fact that the enclosed polar wire becomes not only self-luminous, but that it is surrounded in addition with a corkscrew formation of light, spinning around it in an impetuous current. One would think that this fact alone would arouse the most sympathetic interest on the part of the physicists. What they have discovered with an endless expenditure of acumen, every child, so to speak, if it is but a sensitive, can hold within its grasp and describe to them with all accompanying circumstances as something perceived by the senses—the Ampère spiral of the voltaic current. After all, there must be some physicists who are themselves sensitives : so, at least, we should expect ; and personally I have come across at least a dozen medical practitioners who are such. But as to how long it will take to awaken the interest of physicists in general, I must confess that I do not know.

Heat and electricity, consequently, are powerful sources of od, but I must refrain for the present from setting forth the abundance of the phenomena which they give rise to.[1] I wish instead to introduce you to the last and most important of these sources of od.

Captain Anschütz, now on service in the Austrian army, who is a good medium-sensitive, once lay ill in Baden, and during this illness his sensitivity to excitation was enormously increased. As he lay sleepless on his bed, it became apparent to him that, when the nights were very dark, he could see the finger-plates, the hinges, and the lock of the door opposite, though he was unable to make out any other object in the room. He recognized the fact that the objects mentioned were apparently self-luminants. Other persons, none, however, who were not high-sensitives, observed all the metal plates on the furniture, all the locks, all the gilt objects in their

[1] Further details are to be found in the publication already quoted : Reichenbach's *Dynamids in their Relation to Vital Energy*, etc.

room, and every nail on the wall, to be luminous and emitting tiny flames or luminous smoke.

I drew up a small specimen-sheet of a number of metals ; these were found by all high-sensitives to be slightly luminous, some more, others less clearly so ; but to all the sensitives all of them were at least visible. A glazed cabinet filled with an assortment of silver-plate appeared in the darkness to be replete with a fine fire.

When I tried substances of another character— coal, selenium, iodine, sulphur—they too were found to be luminous. The appearance of these bodies resembled the glow of phosphorescence, so that they looked as if they were transparent ; they could be seen right into.

Together with the glow, high-sensitives observed surrounding these substances the same flame-like emanation of light losing itself in smoke, as is already known to us from other concentrated outflowings of od. In this as in the former cases the emanation could be made to flicker and flutter by the breath, or by a draught in the room, and was in many cases capable of lighting up the fingers which held the objects undergoing observation.

In colour the emanations were found to be by no means alike, and this fact afforded a safe means for checking the exactness of the observations. Every- thing made of copper, for instance, was seen in a red glow, surrounded by a green flame ; tin, lead, palladium and cobalt were blue ; bismuth, zinc, osmium, titanium, potassium, red ; silver, gold, platinum, antimony, cadmium, white ; nickel and chromium, a kind of green, shading off into a greenish- yellow ; iron almost polychrome, playing with all the colours of the rainbow ; arsenic, coal, iodine, and selenium, red ; sulphur, blue, and sulphur itself was often seen as blue by medium-sensitives.

Chemical compositions were also luminous, and some of them so to a remarkably high degree ; theobromine, e.g., was white ; parabanic acid, a remarkably fine blue ; and calcined lime, red. I made a portable collection of several hundred chemical preparations rowed closely together, kept them in the dark, and only opened them again in the darkness of the *camera obscura*. Medium-sensitives only saw a few of them ; but high-sensitives saw them all without exception, in a weaker or stronger degree of luminosity. Even the masonry of the walls of the dark chamber showed up after a fairly long period in the darkness as emitting a fine, rather white light. This went so far that my seers were finally able to see everything in the room in a kind of twilight, and even took me by the arm, as I, of course, could see nothing at all, and led me about with the greatest certainty amidst all my scientific instruments.

Everything, then, emits light ; everything, everything ! We live in a world full of shining matter. Just as an impetuous eruption of light takes place in the sun, so on earth an extremely feeble emission of light takes place, quite uniformly, from everything to be found there. Flimsy substances, such as cottons, woollens, wood, glue, etc., show the feeblest degree of luminosity. All kinds of stone are luminous. The most brilliantly luminous among amorphous substances are the metals, and the simple elements in general. This source of a luminosity common to everything in the universe is feebler in degree than any of the sources of light previously mentioned ; but, as a set-off against that, it is unlimited in extent.

Well, is this luminosity odic ? It is ; because it

has all the characteristics of od, including the effects produced by all od-containers on the sense of feeling. Lay any metals you like—say sulphur, iodine, coal, graphite—on any kind of board—say a plank of limewood—and get strongly sensitive persons to pass the palm of their left hand over them ; you will find that they feel themselves affected by coolness or lukewarmth, with a sense of comfort or discomfort, and that most strongly by the substances that shine the brightest, and most feebly, down to not at all, by those whose light is dullest.

Or, put substances of all sorts confusedly, solids and liquids, open or hermetically sealed in glass vessels, into the hand of strongly sensitive persons, be the hand bare or gloved ; they will have a different sensation from each, of coolness or lukewarmth, of liking or of dislike, while in the case of many they will have that sensation connected with special secondary effects, e.g. in the case of sulphur, bromine, bichromate of potassium, oxygenated gas, arsenic, quicksilver, and copper. They will distinguish each by their feeling, and classify each according to its odic character.

Od, therefore, not only flows in concentrated form from special sources, but is, in addition, a general endowment of the whole of Nature, a variously shared but universally distributed natural force, such as heat, electricity, chemical affinity, gravity, etc. It interpenetrates and fills the structure of the universe, present in the smallest things as well as in the greatest.

XI

EXAMPLES FROM THE WORLD OF MATTER

YOU will remember my saying, no doubt, that there are numerous instances of the prettiest of girls avoiding the presence of mirrors? You will have gathered the explanation of this singular phenomenon from the contents of my last letter. Quicksilver is one of the metals that have the most nauseating reaction on sensitive human beings. When one of the latter goes near a large-surfaced mirror, he feels the unpleasant effect of the quicksilver diffused over his entire body ; it seems to him as though a lukewarm sickly breath came upon him ; he feels himself pushed and driven off and, if he chooses to resist, he is attacked by stomach-ache, a feeling of in-disposition, headache, and even vomiting ; he has to give way. This attains to such a pitch with increasing experience that, in the case of high-sensitives, it leads to shuddering in the presence of a mirror, so that they cover it up when they cannot put it out of the way.

Let us now, please, glance back at the subject of disgust as caused by tablespoons of German silver, argentan, new silver, and Chinese silver. Copper, which forms the foundation in all these compositions, is about as strongly odic a body as you can get for a very nauseating and disgusting reaction. Electro-plate it as you will, it is all in vain ; the copper exercises its odic effect from beneath the plating, becomes unbearable even to medium-sensitives, and as to high-sensitives, it not unfrequently causes them stomach-ache, and even cramp of the tongue and lockjaw. I have often enough heard lady sensitives say that they can wear no metal ornaments, because they do not feel comfortable with them ; that they cannot bear working with a metal thimble, and must have an ivory one ; that they cannot fix a steel busk to their corsets ; nay, that they cannot even endure hairpins in their hair—and all simply on account of the disagreeably tepid odic reaction of the metal.

To sensitive girls engaged in domestic service brass pestles and mortars, copper cooking utensils, and particularly flat-irons made of metal, are an abomination. Our respected mill-owner of Azgersdorf (near Vienna), Mr. J. Fichtner, a good medium-sensitive, has had all brass utensils removed from his kitchen, as he cannot bear partaking of food or drink that has been prepared in brass.

Though metals be covered over with paper, linen, or other light substances, high-sensitives are always able to detect where the pieces of metal lie hidden, merely by the sense of feeling in the palm of their left hand which they hold above. In this connection can you fail to remember the ninth letter of this series, in which I spoke of friction by water and Monsieur Sourcier ? Given the presence of metals, say a sum of money in coinage to a fair amount buried underground, but not too deep beneath the surface, there can be no doubt that a high-sensitive would discover such objects by his sense of feeling, more easily and quickly than the sensitives of medium powers found out the water-conduit in my grounds.

Now take the case of a vein of lead-glance, copper pyrites, red silver ore, and the like, cropping up not too far beneath the surface—as they are so often found to lie hidden a few feet only beneath the vegetable soil—and of a high-sensitive directing his steps above them with some degree of attention ; can you doubt even for a moment, after what you now know, that he would become aware of them through his sensations, and would be able to point out the exact spot where they are located ?

And other things too, such as the outcrops of coal-beds, are sure to have a quite different effect on a man highly sensitive to odic excitation, than the sandstone and shale in which they lie. When such a man has previously observed the odic sensations produced upon him by masses of coal, and recorded them in his memory, he will at once be able to tell when he is walking over a coal-bed. No other man will be able to perceive anything of the matter, but a high-sensitive will tell you straight off with perfect assurance : there, or there beyond, this mineral or that lies underground ; and excavation will justify the apparent miracle ; which up to the present has seemed all the more astonishing from the fact that the finder has been unable to account to himself satisfactorily for the matter, and much less to anyone else.

The miracle is now made plain ; it is nothing else than a purely physical influence of the odic dynamid on the human nervous system ; it takes effect like an occult sense, about which no one is in a position to draw any conclusion ; and a large number of the incidents ascribable to instinct in animals will find their explanation on the same lines as those I have just given for the metal- and ore-finder.

And now, my friend, there you have in their completeness the final secrets of the divining-rod, not, it is true, of the rod as such in its literal sense, with its alleged dipping and twisting and thrashing out—I take all that to have been nothing more than the hocus-pocus of the art, contrived for the curious multitude, to whom those pestered by their enquiries had to give some tangible reply—but of the hitherto deep-hid, substantial kernel of the matter.

The perception of the sensitive can be uncommonly developed by practice. When I get new people to deal with, their indications are sometimes strikingly subject to fluctuation, and it is only after two or three sittings that everything begins to clear up and become definite. But a prolonged period of practice in these perceptions brings decision and readiness, and I have medium-sensitives who, in virtue of a six and seven years' familiarity, have attained to an acuteness of discrimination that more often than not makes them superior to nigh-sensitives who are novices.

Such men will in future be of great utility in relation to the counterfeiting of goods. Anyone who is a good sensitive is fairly sure to possess the faculty of distinguishing genuine gold and silver from the plating on copper. But this faculty can be extended by practice for all sorts of mixtures, so much so that the stock in a druggist's shop, for instance, could be judged in the matter of its retention or loss of efficient principles. Indeed, I shall perhaps show you later on what astonishing diagnoses of sick patients can be obtained from the mere sense of feeling exerted by sensitives in good health.

XII

Odic Discharge and Conduction—Approach

You are now acquainted with the most important sources of od, at least so far as I have succeeded in discovering them up to the present. Crystals, sun and moon, magnets, plants, beasts and men, chemical reaction, together with fermentation and decomposition, sound, friction with the movement of water, heat, electricity, and finally the whole world of matter in regularly determined degrees of strength, all these emit the remarkable phenomena perceptible to feeling and sight which we cannot assign to any of the known forces, but all of which present a single common point of view from which their connection may be recognized, and which must consequently be dealt with as an independent branch of physical science. Let us now consider the principle which must be regarded as their basis with regard to certain of its characteristics.

The first characteristic we come upon is that of its transference from one body to another, that is to say, its dischargeability. When a hot or electrified body is brought into contact with another, it makes the latter also hot or electrified ; it is then said that the force in question permits of discharge. Od behaves in the same way. You have seen how a glass of water held to the pole of a crystal or magnet, or connected with a glass rod subjected to friction, or set in sun- or moonlight, or brought into the blue or red colours of the rainbow, took on an odic quality. And for the glass of water you may substitute any other body you like. Take a little bit of wood, a

66

clew of yarn, your watch, a china plate, a small stone, a piece of sugar, whatever chances to come into your hand ; let the sensitive hand first hold it and test it for a moment ; then put it for a short time, a few minutes, say, before a pole that is giving out od, and finally give it back to the sensitive, into the same hand as before. He will find it altered ; he will tell you that he gets it back warmer or cooler.

And, mark you, he will find it altered in the very sense in which the odic source to which you exposed the object under examination would have affected him, and not in the contrary sense, as magnetism in such cases brings about in iron. What takes place, therefore, is nothing else than the fact that the od-emitting pole has brought the neutral object set within its sphere of action into the same odic condition as that with which it itself was overflowing. This is communication, discharge—to be carefully distinguished in the case from induction, the former being an odic form of activity, the latter a mode of influencing other bodies peculiar to magnets.

All those glasses of water, consequently, which you have seen exposed by me time and again to sources of od, were charged with od ; they were odified ; and the alteration which took place in them must be regarded as analogous with that which takes place in a glass of water when it is warmed or chilled. It is the same water ; nothing tangible has entered into its composition ; a dynamic change alone has been effected in it by the operation, but, remarkably enough, a change that exercises an effect at the same time upon the sense of the taster.

You can prove the same also with regard to illuminating power. Hang a copper wire with one end in the dark chamber and the other in the light of day outside, and bring up to the latter in turn a strong crystalline pole, a magnetic pole, one of your two hands, or keep rubbing it with a file, or put it into a glass in which you dissolve an effervescing powder in small successive quantities, or hold it over a charcoal fire, or bring it within the sphere of distribution of an electrical conductor—in all these cases your sensitive will see the wire become luminous in the darkness, and a small smoking flame dotted with sparks streaming from its extremity, so long as you keep up your action on the wire. The od discharged upon the wire will convert it to a higher power of illumination and, visibly to the sensitive eye, stream forth from its extremity, losing itself at last in the surrounding air.

A continual current of od into the atmosphere takes place in the same way from your finger-tips, from the tips of your toes, and from your whole body. This separation into the atmosphere is nothing else than a true discharge of od. One of the strongest discharges of this kind takes place from the breath of all living creatures. In the lungs, as is well known, a very vigorous chemical reaction takes place on the inspiration of air ; as a consequence of this, od is set in motion according to rule, and discharges itself upon the air of respiration, which is thus breathed out, carrying a strong odic charge. Mrs. Cecily Bauer, the wife of a hotel-keeper in Vienna, a very strong woman in robust health and at the same time strongly sensitive, told me with some anxiety that, whenever she woke up on a dark night and could distinguish nothing in the room, she could still always see her husband and her child in a sort of light as they lay asleep at her side, and that, whenever they breathed out, shining clouds of vapour came out of the mouths of both. That is the od-laden breath, which nearly all sensitives see coming out of their own mouths in the darkness like clouds of tobacco-smoke.

Recur now in thought to my first letter, where I referred to the crowded car of an omnibus or railway-train, in which a sensitive is sitting, hemmed in among other people, a man on whom the reaction of all "like" od has a disagreeable effect. Now the atmosphere in a narrow, closed-in space of that sort becomes completely charged, and overcharged, with od from the bodies of many people and the breath of so many lungs in quite a short space of time, and the sensitive cannot draw in a single breath without taking in at the same time air that is just as strongly charged as that which it is an unavoidable necessity to him to breathe out. And now imagine yourself in the position of this tortured man, when the opening of the carriage-window is refused him. He is there upon the rack, and no one recognizes the fact that he is suffering. From this time forth, however, it may be trusted that you will give him your sympathy and help.

In the same way it will now become clear to you why a high-sensitive cannot stay in a crowded company, and least of all in rooms that have not got a very high ceiling. The air soon becomes overcharged with od : he gets uneasy, hot, suffering more than he can endure, and if he cannot get away he loses his temper, and becomes irritable and inclined to be vexed at the smallest thing. And the longer he has to stay, the more he gets out of humour.

It is just the same with sensitives in bed. They charge their pillows, coverings, and mattresses with their own odic emanations. This soon becomes repugnant and disturbing to them. They twist and turn from this side to that the whole night through, get rid of their covering, and are only to some degree at rest when they are lying without anything over them at all.

A man of high-sensitivity is always a restless being, literally a *mauvais coucheur*, and must be so from his very nature. He is continually charging all his clothes with an od from his own body that is polarically like to that of the part they cover. The clothes and the parts of the body act and react upon each other with charges of " like " character, and produce the sickly warmth complained of. Thus the sensitive always feels worried when he keeps still, and only finds relief when in movement and getting rid of his od into the air. The consequence is that he can only bear very light clothing ; everything he wears always seems too much for him. Though he change his position and his occupation continually, he is subject to an unceasing sense of oppression.

Od admits not only of discharge into all other bodies, but also of *conduction*. We have just encountered a proof of this in the rod held by the sensitive in the sunshine. The od from the sunshine, the heliod we may call it, passed along the rod into his hand. Now, however, make up a composite rod artificially ; set one of metal alongside one of wood ; attach a wax candle to the two, and last of all twine round a silken cord. Put this four-part rod by the end of the stick into the sensitive's left hand and, after giving him about half a minute to grow accustomed to the feel of it, take hold of the silken cord with the fingers of your right hand. You will hear after a few seconds that the rod is getting cool ; change the cord to your left hand and he will slew round to a sense of the sickly-soft sensation.

If you bring the silk cord into contact with the pole of a crystal, with a spectrum, with moonlight, with effervescing water, with sulphur, in every case you will conduct the effects proper to the source of od at work ; they will all course along to the sensitive hand through the substances according to their varying degrees of conductivity. Make up conductors of sulphur, glass, silk, resin, india-rubber, or any idio-electrical substance you please, and they will all conduct od just as well as the metals do. For this dynamid there is no isolator. Therein lies the difficulty it sets in the path of all investigation.

In all the experiments described it is not even necessary that the rod which the sensitive holds by one end should be set in actual contact with the odic sources ; mere *approximation* is quite enough. Put a glass rod in his hand, and bring your own finger-tips near the other end without touching it at any point. You will soon find out that you are exercising, if a somewhat weaker, at any rate a qualitatively quite similar, effect upon the rod and the hand of the sensitive. Set the pole of a crystal, a hare's foot, a dose of bichromate of potassium dissolved in water, a bit of sulphur, a bottle of fermenting wine-must, merely in the close neighbourhood of such a rod, and the sensitive's hand will experience the corresponding reaction forthwith. This is in every point in agreement with the luminous emanations from all these odic sources. Good conductors such as the metals, glass, and silk become luminous from every fairly strong discharge or conduction, and clothe themselves throughout their length with a luminous covering of vapour, whether worked upon by actual contact or only by approach.

XIII

Odic Dualism

WHEREVER we look in Nature, we come across examples of *duality in material objects*, and their presence does not fail in the field we occupy now. You have already met them in the case of the crystals, the magnets, the two halves of animals and men, where you always found on one side reddish-yellow od-light with disagreeable sensations of lukewarmness, and on the other side blue light with pleasant sensations of coolness. But the contrast appears in innumerable cases among the odic phenomena ; it belongs to the very essence of that force.

This time let us take the simple substances of chemistry as our starting-point. Give your sensitive in turns a small phial of potassium and another of pulverized sulphur, placing them in his left hand. You will shortly receive his pronouncement that the former is having a sickly, disagreeable effect upon his feelings, and the latter a cool and pleasant one. Do the same with sodium, gold, platinum, mercury, and copper, on the one side, and selenium, iodine, phosphorus, tellurium, and arsenic on the other, and you will get the sickly, disagreeable effect from the former elements and the cool effect from the latter, a little stronger or a little weaker in the case of each.

You can proceed to make use of this graduated difference of odic strength in the simple substances for their tabulation in a series, at one end of which stands potassium as the most disagreeably lukewarm of all, and at the other end oxygen as the coolest of all ; and when you carefully consider the series you have constructed, you will be astonished to find that, with trifling departures, it agrees with the series chemistry gives us in reference to the power of affinity to oxygen, known as the electro-chemical series [*or series of atomic weights*]. We have arrived at the same result along quite another path, namely, an equivalent series to which we must give the name of the **od-chemical series.**

Is it not surprising in the highest degree that a simple, unschooled girl, by the mere feeling in her fingers alone, is able within one hour to classify all the elements in Nature into a series, the construction of which has cost the greatest minds and the most learned men of our times more than half a century of tireless industry and the utmost efforts of their mental acumen ? The great Berzelius, the creator of the electro-chemical system, had a profound sense of this fact when I laid the proofs before him in Carlsbad in the year 1845 ; but since his death surviving chemists have not thought so trifling a matter worthy of any further attention. One physiologist even has not wanted the courage to accuse the dead Berzelius of senility, because he had expressly and publicly assumed the patronage of these results of my researches.[1] To help out the impetuosity of his own judgment, he needed nothing less than the modest assurance that Berzelius had on this occasion lost the use of his senses.

Of course the amorphous bodies, each taken by itself, make no exhibition of dual characteristics in this odic series, and must be regarded in each instance as unipolar, pretty much as the electrical scientists regarded soap as unipolar. The series, however, embraces them in their universality, and, taking

---

[1] Mr. Emil Du Bois-Reymond of Berlin. See Karsten's *Fortschritte der Physik* (*Advances of Physical Science*), 3rd year, p. 401.

them in this as a collective unit of the world of matter, the amorphous substances serve to emphasize the contrast in which soft, sickly sensations are produced in the sensitive hand at one end of the series and sensations of coolness at the other. **Odic polarity exists in the world of matter;** and, as the warm-felt substances on the left are the electro-positive and the cool-felt substances on the right the electro-negative, I must in the like sense and as a matter of consistency name the former **odpositive** and the latter **odnegative.**

Among composite substances, I have found the alkalis and alkaloids and everything marked by the alkaline characteristics to be odpositive, and on the other hand the haloid salts and the greater number of the oxides and acids to be odnegative, the organic substances such as rubber, starch, many of the heavy oils, and paraffin also, occupying in this respect a middle position.

In the matter of crystals, I have found that the side on which they started their growth always declares itself to the sensitive's left as sickly-warm to the touch and red-yellow to the sight, while the upper peak to which they continued their growth expresses itself as cool and blue-lit. This rule can be traced as far as the fibrous crystallizations, and up to the point of the torpid congelations where the crystalline structure itself ceases almost to be traceable. According to rule, then, the cleavage line of the crystal is odpositive, and the peak odnegative.

As to the magnet, its southward pole feels tepid to the sensitive's left and shows him a red light; that is to say, it is odpositive. Its northward pole is similarly sensed as cool and blue-lit; it is therefore odnegative. (Some physicists, but not all—see Liebig's *Manual of Chemistry*, v., p. 34—give the northward pole of the magnetic needle as magneto-positive, without furnishing any definite reason for their so doing. In view of odic data I must doubt the accuracy of this. Odpositive and electro-positive bodies go hand in hand, as we have seen, and magneto-positive bodies must keep in step with them ; consequently the northward pole of the needle, which shows a blue light, can only be magneto-negative.) Heat, chemical reaction, and sound, have in the course of the previous investigations shown purely odnegative effects, and friction only odpositive. Researches into the odic contrasts must be extended further in regard to this point.

Polarized sunlight is odpositive in the refracted, and odnegative in the reflected, rays. In the spectrum the red, orange and yellow rays, and the rays ranged under red are all odpositive ; the blue, violet and chemical rays are odnegative. The same holds good for the lunar spectrum ; and it even holds good for the weak spectrum of an Argand lamp.

The animal, and in particular the human, body shows itself positively odic on the whole of the left side from the summit of the cranium to the toes, and negatively odic on the whole of the right side. This shows itself most strongly in the toes and finger-tips, and especially at the roots of the finger-nails, the seats of the most vital organic activity in the whole hand. Man is consequently polarised in regard to breadth. He possesses, however, other, though less strongly prominent, odic axes, namely, an axis of length and an axis of thickness, the discussion of which, however, I must refrain from in the restricted space allotted to this journalistic correspondence.

You may confirm yourself in your convictions by a few more easy experiments. Place a sheet of unused, medium-blue paper before a sensitive, and make him look at it first with the left, then with the right, eye in rotation, each time covering the eye he is not using. He will find the glance with the left eye pleasant, and with the right eye unpleasant. The left eye is odpositive and the blue tint works, as we already know, odnegatively; unlike agencies therefore met, and the effect was a pleasant one. In the other case, in which the right eye looked upon the blue, like agencies met, and the sensation of the effect was disagreeable.

Check the experiment with a sheet of orange-coloured paper ; you will always get the same results, but vice versa as regards the eyes. You also see, however, from this delicate experiment, that the disagreeableness of the yellow and the pleasantness of the blue to sensitives is more especially based upon the view taken by the left eye, and that the effect upon the consciousness is predominant upon this side, and notably more important than the effect upon the right. [*Note this obiter dictum as important.*]

Look with your right eye at a short distance into the left eye of the sensitive, and he will raise no objection. (It is to be understood that while this takes place the other two eyes are to be closed.) Now look with your left eye into his left, and he will at once grow uneasy, and will not allow himself to be detained for half a minute. He will not be able to endure your glance ; and, if you wish to make him, he will turn away. Should he be a high-sensitive, a short optical fixation of that sort will have such an unpleasantly strong effect upon him that in a few seconds later he will see nothing more out of that particular eye ; indeed, it will often happen, if you force him to continue, that he will have to vomit.

Left looking into left makes "like" pairing, and as such becomes unendurable to him.

Is odic dualism ascertainably present in the opposition of *the two sexes*? I put this question to Nature by means of the following simple experiment : I stationed a man and a woman opposite a female sensitive, and set a glass of water in the right hand of each. After six minutes, during which the water must have been negatively odified, I got the sensitive to taste from each glass. She found both cool, but the one she received from the man's hand far cooler and more agreeable than that which she received from the woman's. Upon this I stationed the pair opposite a male sensitive and went through the same proceeding. He, however, found the water from the woman's hand the cooler. You see clearly : man and woman stand in odpolar opposition.

You have no doubt remarked that I have always requisitioned your sensitive's left hand for these experiments in the sense of feeling and never his right. I must now make you clear as to the reason. " Cool " and " lukewarm " are not absolute effects of outward stimulus to the subject of excitability, but only relative effects, in relation to one specified side of the body ; on the other side the sensation is the opposite. But to prevent confusion of any sort entering into my descriptions, I made all the experiments only in relation to one side, and that side the left, because effects as a rule are stronger and more clearly marked on that side, and are also in consequence perceived with a more special precision. I might just as well have chosen the right side : the results would have been the same, only vice versa as regards lights and sensations.[1]

[1] Cf. the dualistic philosophy of the oldest Scotic druids.

XIV

THE ODIC SPECTRUM—THE POLARITY OF THE EARTH

YOUR heart has been uplifted many a time by the glory of the rainbow, in the full light of day. I am going to introduce you now to a rainbow in the darkness of the night.

When seated with a crystal in the dark, a weak-sensitive sees nothing more at its two poles than a greyish, ill-defined cloud, a dull luminosity in the midst of the general night. A medium-sensitive draws a distinction : to *him* the brightness at one of the poles is bluish grey and blue, and at the other yellow and yellowish-red, corresponding with his own right and left hands. Finally a sensitive of higher degree recognizes that neither the blue nor the yellow is a simple colour, but that within it in each case other tints of all sorts—green, red, orange, violet—dart in and out of each other, and that each of the polar flames, when more narrowly observed, presents a polychrome appearance, always understanding this, however, in the sense that what we have just referred to are secondary shades, subordinate flecks of colour, in the general blue of the one pole and the general red of the other.

It was a sensitive naval pensioner, Frederick Weidlich, who first drew my attention, in February 1846, to the fact that these colours did not always play in and out of each other in this restless way, but that they lay over each other in repose, and took up a regular order, when not disturbed and mingled together by the current of air caused by my movements and breathing. And when I enquired as to

78

the order they took up, I learnt that red, clouded by a deal of smoke, always took up the lowest place, and that over it first reddish-yellow, then saffron-yellow, then pale-yellow, on that finch-yellow, and then green appeared, that the latter shaded into blue, first a light-blue and then a dark, and that on top of all appeared a violet-red, which finally lost itself in smoky vapour, and that the whole was intermingled with a great number of tiny, brightly luminous sparks or little stars.

What I learnt for the first time from this man I was told subsequently by numerous sensitives in thousands of experiments made by night. Now, what else is this than the colour arrangement of the prismatic spectrum? The phenomenon of a rainbow of light in absolute darkness—what a marvellous sight! All high-sensitives described it to me as the most beautiful they had ever looked upon in their lives.

I set up a strong rod-magnet vertically on end, with its southward pole uppermost; a reddish tint dominated all the rainbow colours that layered themselves over it in repose. I reversed it, setting its northward pole uppermost, and a bluish colouration lay upon the dulled-off bow. The section of the rod at the poles was a square inch. In order to narrow this surface, I put a pointed iron cap upon it; the emanation of light became thinner, more luminous and longer, but the rainbow order of the colours remained constant.

Instead of the single-pointed cap, I next set an iron cap with two peaks upon it: lights now jutted out of both, but quite a blue light from one of them, and a yellow-red light from the other. Finally I put a four-peaked cap on it, and now each peak showed a differently coloured body of light ; the first had a small blue flame, the second a yellow, the third a red, the fourth a whitish grey : all four stood straight up vertically, side by side, from the four corners of the magnet-rod.   I had thus succeeded in separating some of the colours of this mysterious iris, and setting up each independently, so to speak, of the others.

When I turned the rod slowly round on its vertical axis, the colours did not go along with it, but each kept its own place, and when the peak with the originally yellow flame came to the spot previously occupied by the peak with the blue flame, the yellow had passed over into blue, the blue into grey, the grey into red, and so forth.   The colours thus were not dependent on the rod alone, but stood in connection with some other exterior condition.   The meaning of this was soon discovered : it was the quarters of the globe that influenced the colours of the rod. The blue light kept always on the peak that was directed towards N., the yellow on that towards W., the red on that towards S., and the grey-white on that towards E.   I might turn the rod round with its four peaks as I chose, the colours never deserted their spot, but maintained the same position with one another in respect to the same quarter of the heavens.

Instead of the four upright peaks, I then fixed a four-cornered plate of iron with a square foot of surface lying horizontally on my rod-magnet.   It had scarcely lain on the pole when coloured lights streamed out horizontally from all its four corners, just as the vertical lights had proceeded from the four peaks. When I turned the plate round a half-quadrant, the mixed colours presented themselves at the four corners, at N.W. green, at S.W. orange, at S.E. grey-red, and at N.E. violet.

I now brought a round sheet of iron into play, and laid it on the standing rod of the magnet. The beautiful formation of a circular rainbow arose out of the darkness. Light streamed forth all round the edge of the sheet. From N. it went through all shades of blue into all of green, thence to W. in shadings of greenish-yellow into yellow and orange-red, to S. in full red and greyish-red, then to E. in grey ; at N.E. a fairly sharply defined red band stood out distinctly from the rest, and finally, on approaching N., the blue tints presented themselves again.

Upon this I had a hollow sphere of iron made, so large that I could not quite embrace its circumference with both my arms, and suspended it, hanging freely, by a silken cord in the midst of my dark chamber. Passing right through its centre I fixed a vertical iron rod, twined round with six coatings of copper wire, which I could connect with a Smee and Young's electric battery of zinc and silver plates. Nothing of this was visible exteriorly. At the moment I converted the iron rod into an electro-magnet my sensitives saw the suspended sphere emerge from the darkness in multi-coloured light. Its whole surface shone gaily with all the colours of the rainbow. The segments turned towards N. were blue from pole to pole, those towards N.W. green, those towards W. yellow, towards S.W. burnt yellow, towards S. red, towards S.E. greyish-red, towards E. grey, and towards N.E. a red stripe, with a recurrence of the blue. The colours visibly formed fine lines one beside the other, separated in each case by a darker line. The whole sphere was enveloped in a fine, luminous, englobing body of vapour.

The upper, odnegative half had at all points a more bluish sheen dominating its other colours, and the lower odpositive half one more inclined to red. Right on top, on the spot where the northward pole of the electro-magnet was situate, a column of light, passing into blue, mounted to the height of a hand over the sphere, then bent back on all sides like an opened umbrella, and streamed down round about the sphere, at a distance of two to three inches from it. From the other pole, the southward one underneath, proceeded a similar bunch of flame, bending up round the sphere with a reddish light. They both became threadbare and lost before reaching the equator of the sphere.

A light is thrown on the matter when I say that my intention was to set up by means of this sphere a terrestrial globe according to Barlow, that is a small sphere in suspension, shaped like the earth, with a north and a south pole, equipped with the magnetic forces proper to it, and applied to the touchstone of the od-light. It is seen in fact that the results obtained resemble to a surprising degree those of the Northern Lights and the Southern Lights of our planet. More detailed resemblances than are here permissible to the demonstrator are obtainable by further parallelizing, and in such perfection that the hypothesis of the Northern Lights being positive od-light is one that has every probability in its favour.

We see, then, that all od-light phenomena are not monochrome, but are analysable, on closer observation into a regular iris.

XV

Terrestrial Magnetism and Terrestrial Od

If the stratification of the od-light colouration takes place in accordance with the direction of the heavens, as you have learnt from my last letter, the fact must have something in itself which stands in close relationship with od. If a pocket-magnet can influence these things in virtue of its odic content, it is evident at first glance that magnetism emanating from such a mighty container as the whole sphere of the earth, that is, **terrestrial magnetism,** must similarly exercise the greatest influence on each and every odic phenomenon within our sphere. This influence is none other than that of the od which is everywhere allied with magnetism, that is consequently also associated with the magnetic poles of the earth, and, starting from them, is in action over the entire planet. It might be referred to congruously as **terrestrial od.**

You have seen how the pole of the magnet which yields odic coolness to the left hand, as all electrically negative bodies do, turns to the N. when it receives freedom of action in the binnacle-box; we should consequently, then, recognize it as negative, and also the od associated with it. And, as the terrestrial pole which attracts it in this direction can only be an unlike one, it follows that the north pole of our earth must be odpositive and the south pole odnegative. It follows further, from that, that the whole northern hemisphere of the earth must be odpositive in its action, and the whole southern hemisphere odnegative.

We should like now to make a nearly related application of this fact to our daily life. I drew your attention in the first of these letters to the fact that all sensitives cannot sleep upon the left, but only on the right, side. I can trust myself with all confidence to express the opinion that this will not be the case in New Holland, in Chile, or in Buenos Aires, but that, on the contrary, all the sensitives in those parts will only like sleeping on their left. In the neighbourhood of the equator it will be a matter of indifference to them whether they sleep on the left or the right.

It must surely be so. The northern surface of the earth is odically positive. Turn the left or odpositive side of a sensitive to it and you have a like pairing; and this he cannot endure. It has a disagreeably lukewarm, disturbing, sleep-banishing, effect upon him. But now lay your sensitive friend on his odnegative right, and the trouble is removed : unlike pairing comes in ; negative side and positive earth-surface are turned to each other, and the reign of peace and comfort commences. The sensitive falls asleep without more ado. In the southern hemisphere the case is vice versa. There you have the deep-laid reason of an apparently very superficial matter, which pathology may make a note of.

I want now to take in *en passant* a similar fact, and one even more native still to our argument. I have said nothing to you so far—in order to save space—as to the odic character of the longitudinal axis in man. Omitting proofs, then, I wish to make you briefly aware of the fact that I have ascertained the human subject to be odnegative in the upper half from the brain downwards, and odpositive in the lower half from the waist downwards. With this as premiss, I ask you to place four chairs in the centre of a room, turning the back of one to the (magnetic) north, that of another to the west, that of the third to the south, and that of the fourth to the east. Now ask a good sensitive if it would be a matter of indifference to him on which of the four seats he should be compelled to remain for some time. When he has tried all of them in turn, he will decide that he feels most comfortable on the one in which he turns his back to the north and his face to the south, and most uncomfortable on the one in which he turns his back to the west and his face to the east.

From the qualities he attributes to the other seats, I shall hurry on to invite you to extend the experiment you have made with your sensitive's seats to his bed. Get him to lie down on it, and then move him and bed together with the head turned towards the four quarters of the globe in rotation. He will soon let you know that he feels most comfortable in the position in which he has his head to the north and his feet to the south. The explanation is to hand at once. The upper half of his body, in relation to the axis of length, is odnegative, the north pole of the earth odpositive. When the two are turned towards each other, the result is an unlike, that is, an acceptable, pairing. The lower half of his body is odpositive, and makes an unlike contrast with the negative south pole of the earth. Every other position, sitting or lying, is less suitable, and more or less unpleasant, distasteful, disquieting.

There are some of my sensitives who, since imbibing this teaching from me, always take a compass with them when they travel, and in every hotel they stop at set their bedstead by the magnetic needle. I have known high-sensitives incapable of getting proper rest in any other than the N. to S. position. But even medium-sensitives and sensitives of a low degree of sensitivity, such as Mr. Delhez for instance, the French language teacher in Vienna, are so powerfully influenced by the position of their bed that it is a deciding factor not only in the matter of their night's rest, but also, and consequently, in that of their general condition of health. A sensitive in good health should therefore note it as a dietetic rule always to have the head of his bed turned to the north ; but a sick patient who is a sensitive simply must, and before everything else, be brought into this orientation ; without it every other effort made for his cure, and all medical treatment, are well nigh in vain.

I can now return with you to the church, where I left you in my first letter by the side of the people who had fainted. We have adopted as a rule of ecclesiastical architecture a custom we have inherited from our heathen ancestors, namely, to set the altar at the east end of the building, and the nave consequently points to the end opposite. In consequence of this arrangement the congregation sit facing the altar with their backs towards the west. But, as we saw, that is exactly the orientation the sensitive is least of all able to endure. His odpositive left is turned thereby to the odpositive terrestrial north pole, and his odnegative right at the same time to the odnegative south pole. He is sitting consequently in a position subjected to a double action of like pairings, and this it is not in his power to hold out against. If it lasts for a considerable time, such as the time taken to sit through a whole church service, and his degree of sensitivity is not low, one discomfort befalls him after another, he gets hot, feels restless and ill at ease, is troubled by migraine or sickness of the stomach, then by stomach-ache, and if he is not able to slip out, he ends up by falling down in a swoon. This is what we see taking place in great churches every day, and there is nothing else to blame for it but the inappropriate orientation of the building.

But the matter extends also to the daily life we lead in our homes. No chair, or sofa, or seat of any description, should be so placed that any sensitive, taking it, has to turn his back to the west. Even standing with his back to the west he finds insufferable.

Major Philippi, of the Engineers, who is a good medium-sensitive and an experienced seaman, never needs a compass when he is on board ship to be able to tell the four quarters of the heavens ; he has only to turn slowly round as he stands, and he soon feels out clearly the direction of the north and the west. Any sailor who is a sensitive will soon learn to do the same, and find out the pole by the same law as that by which the sensitive dowser felt out the running water.

These things are so mixed up with our everyday life that they should decide, for instance, in the matter of placing a piece of furniture, a machine, or a piano. A lady who was a sensitive used often to play the piano in my home. But she never felt comfortable when she was at it, and could not tell how it was that a feeling of not being up to the mark used to come over her whenever she sat down to my instrument, which, apart from this, was quite a good one. After thinking the matter over for a little, I reflected at last that the sides of the piano, a grand, were set along the meridian, and the lady, when playing, sat at their south pole, with her back turned to the south. That meant that she was sitting with her face towards the odpositive poles of just so many long magnets as there were steel wires stretched in her direction. Against such a combination she had no power of resistance, and, had she remained seated thus for a considerable time, she would have fallen from her chair in a swoon.

I turned the keyboard round, so that she sat at the north end of the instrument and simply faced the northward poles of the magnets. Now everything went well in a trice, and she played with comfort and pleasure. A grand pianoforte, consequently, should never be set so that the performer has to sit south or west of it ; no sensitive could feel well with it that way.

I know a man who was once a fine manager of a household and an industrious weaver, and was at the same time endowed with a considerable degree of sensitivity. He moved to another house, and from that hour had no longer any affection for his loom. He could never sit down upon his weaving-stool without getting the fidgets, took to the tavern and the beershop, neglected his work, and went to ruin. In his old home the loom stood in the northerly direction for the worker's back, in the new in the westerly ; this last position he was not proof against. The odic trouble, the reason of which he knew not, but whose disagreeable gnawings he had no power to withstand, brought the poor man to destruction. Thousands who have to earn their livelihood in a sedentary position, artisans, sempstresses, writers, officials, artists—particularly painters, who let the north light fall upon their work and then sit with their backs to the west, and are in this way bereft of all pleasure in their work—have fallen innocent victims to the hitherto prevailing ignorance of these mysterious physical conditions.

XVI

VELOCITY OF CONDUCTION—RADIATION—RANGE—
ODIC ATMOSPHERE—ODOSCOPE—ETYMOLOGY OF
THE WORD " OD "—CONCLUSION

THE conduction of od through the various substances
is a matter with which you are now acquainted, but
you know nothing as to the **velocity** with which
this takes place. The velocity of electricity is, as
is well known, extremely great, while that of heat is
exceedingly slow ; od holds a sort of middle place
in this respect.

I stretched an iron wire out to the length of 100
feet, and applied various sources of od to its extremity,
one after the other, hands, crystals, and magnets.
A highly sensitive person experienced the arrival
of the corresponding effect in his hand from the other
end of the wire in about half a minute. You can
gather from that that the od advanced slowly enough
along the wire, and could thus be followed in its
course.

You have seen that discharge and conduction could
be effected even without actual contact with the wire,
that is, by simple approach. Whether this took place
by absorption of the light-bearing emanations of the
od-container, or by radiation, we do not yet know.
As to whether od is distributed by radiation at all,
we are not, so far, quite convincingly informed by
the mere facts that od accompanies the rays of the
sun and can be conducted along with them through
glass prisms, therein diffracted, and polarized through
sheets of glass ; because the od resulting from these

incidents couid also perhaps be produced by the impact of the rays of light on the fixed targets.

But take up your stand facing a sensitive, and make the double-handed pass down his person at a distance of half an arm's length : he will feel it quite well, as though a cool breath of air ran down his person. Take a pace further back, and repeat the pass movement in his direction : he will still experience the sensation of coolness, though somewhat more weakly. Go back two, three, or four paces. Your sensitive will still feel your passes, in decreasing strength, it is true, but still definitely enough ; indeed, he would still feel them were you to separate yourself from him by the whole length of the room. Increase your distance from him still further by graduated steps through the neighbouring room : the effect will become weak, but will continue recognizable still. In the case of a person of medium-sensitiveness you can go back in this way to a distance of 40 to 60 feet, until the sensation aroused by your pass becomes uncertain, and finally imperceptible.

A pass from beneath in an upward direction will be perceived at a somewhat greater distance than one from above downwards. But I have had high-sensitives with whom the effect of my hands administering the pass was not exhausted at a distance of 150 feet : I had no greater distance at my disposal, though I had thrown open the doors of my whole suite of rooms. They also felt the poles of the crystal and strong magnets at as great a distance as this, and on the instant, as soon as I had directed the latter upon them.

You see from this that an uncommon degree of radiation is attributable to the force we call od, whose bounds perhaps, like those of light, lie in the infinite. The consequence of this radiant energy is that we carry about with us continually an illimitable train of radiant light which, undetected by our own eyes, sweeps into space from our fingers, toes and limbs, and that, as living beings formed of matter, we are surrounded by a luminous atmosphere of our own, which we take with us wherever we go. I have often heard it remarked in my dark chamber that my head was encircled by a crown of rays, and that I was enveloped in the aureola of a saint. And there can be little doubt that the myth referred to is directly traceable to this phenomenon, whose light was seen thousands of years ago in the East as it is seen here to-day.[1]

This odic atmosphere which every man has about him, and which emanates from every living individual, is not completely similar in every case, but differs somewhat in the case of each, almost as perfumes and flavours differ, as light falls into different colours, and as sound into the various notes of the tonic scale. A woman's differs somewhat from a man's, and a young man's from an old man's ; it differs in the sanguine of temperament from the choleric, and in the healthy from the sick ; and, taking those who are sick, it differs in the case of a catarrh from that of one who has scarlet fever, or typhus fever with its *calor mordax*, etc., and all these differences are perceived and distinctly recognized by high-sensitives, and in many cases often by medium-sensitives.

It is from this fact that you are now for the first time in receipt of a hint as to how it is possible, for instance, that sick patients in extreme conditions of sensibility should recognize the approach of their doctor when the healthy persons around them are still unable to perceive it ; that you yourself should

[1] See quotation from *Aphorisms* on the Human Aura, p. 50.

have so insuperable an objection to many men at the very first meeting, and an unreasoned preference for others ; that beasts of prey and hounds should recognize the trail on a leaf trodden on by their quarry ; and other things of the same sort, which appear to be wonderful, but which only appear so as long as the physical threads are unknown which connect them, quite simply and in accordance with law, in the material world. But I should transgress the bounds which I have accepted for these letters were I to enter upon a description of these higher odic conditions. I therefore now take leave of you.

You now know the phenomenon I have called od in its main outlines. It is a natural force, analogous with, and closely related to, those already known to science. It comprises in a group of its own imponderable, but sensuously perceptible, natural incidents, for which so far we have no other measure or reagent than the human nerve, and that moreover only under the peculiar conditions bound up with the susceptibility of a sensitive. The reason why it has completely escaped scientific investigation up to the present, or rather, why it has been directly and obstinately rebuffed and locked out by science, consists simply in the absence of any general odoscope or odometer which anyone might use, and so prove its existence with ease, and in a way that would appeal to the senses of the entire world.

And the reason, in turn, why no odoscope has so far been invented springs from the very nature of od itself, that is to say, from its power of penetrating all matter and space without incurring congestion at any point, without ever permitting of its densification up to the point of general perceptibility. Heat, electricity, and light have isolators of their own up to a certain point, but I have never been able to discover an isolator for od. I have considered myself called upon to make use of this property of exemption from all obstructibility, in order to form a convenient name for it, pliable enough to adapt itself to the multifarious needs of science. " Va " in Sanskrit means " to move about." " Vado " in Latin and " vada " in Old Norse means " I go quickly, hurry away, stream forth." Hence " Wodan " in Old Germanic expresses the idea of the " All-transcending " ; in the various old idioms it appears as " Wuodan," " Odan," and " Odin," signifying the power penetrating all nature which is ultimately personified as a Germanic deity. " Od " is consequently the word to express a dynamid or force which, with a power that cannot be obstructed, quickly penetrates and courses through everything in the universe.

Had Nature endowed us with a sense of od as clear and distinct as our sense of light and sound, we should stand on a far higher grade of knowledge ; we should distinguish truth from illusion by means of that all-transcending power with incomparably greater ease, rapidity, and certainty than we do at present ; we should see into each other's hearts, as the saying is. A Talleyrand could no longer misuse his speech in order to conceal his thoughts, and we should, as a further result, constitute a higher and nobler order of beings. It would be easy to show how, endowed with a sense of od, we should be something like angels, and that it would only need the gift of such a faculty to raise us straightway to a higher level of morality without having to increase our intellectual powers for the purpose. The All-wise, who only wished for an erring mankind, has had on that account to deny us what would have made us resemble some being half human, half divine.

SUPPLEMENT I

ODIC FORCE AS EXPLANATORY OF CLAIRVOYANCE

THE present volume is issued as a book of "fundamentals," the contention being that these fundamentals still hold good in the main, notwithstanding the advances made since Reichenbach's death in 1869 in all branches of science, among which the advances made in psychic science itself must not be forgotten. It is not intended to set up any foolish contention that rectifications of Reichenbach's work will not be found necessary in instances : but it is for professional scientists to point these instances out. For this reason no attempt is here made to commentate either the text of the *Letters on Odic Magnetism* or that of the passages set on record in this Supplement and Supplement II.

But, as Gustav Theodor Fechner, late professor of physics in the University of Leipsic, remarks in his *Memories of the Last Days of the Odic Theory* [*ad fin.*], Reichenbach's work on psychic phenomena has been so exhaustive, so scientifically conducted, and recorded with such patient precision, that all future investigators will be bound to follow its elaborator along the path on which he is a pioneer, until it is definitely shown what sections of his track, if any, must be abandoned by science.

The two main questions on which students of psychic science have to concentrate their attention in this connection are in my opinion :

1. Is the existence of odic force an objective biological fact?

2. Does odic force, if shown to be objectively existent, explain the phenomena, or lead us towards an explanation of the phenomena, of what is commonly known as " spirit inter- course ? "

The following passages are printed as illuminative texts bearing intimately on the solutions to be given to these two questions :

Prof. Wm. Gregory : *Animal Magnetism*, 4th ed. 1896, pp. 34–36 :

Clairvoyance defined.—Dr. Gregory defines clair- voyance as :

" The direct and immediate perception of absent or distant objects without the use of the eyes."
" Perception in the shape of vision without the use of the external organs of vision."

Q. By what means is the image of the object conveyed to the internal organ of vision and to the sensorium ?

A. " Common vision by ordinary light it cannot be, for the eyes are closed. . . . We must therefore admit the existence of **(a) some other force** or influence, exerted by bodies, and capable of reach- ing the brain without passing through the eye. When the sleeper [*The reference is to the hypnotic patient or " mesmeric sleeper " exercising clairvoyance*] finds his vision not clear, or misty, as he calls it, he will very often, in order to see an object which is shown to him, apply it to his forehead, to the coronal region, or in some rare cases to the occiput, and forthwith perceive it more distinctly. ·

" We feel that he who can see an object behind him while his eyes are closed, and who sees it best when applied to his head, has **some means** of perceiving objects which is either not possessed in the ordinary waking state or, if possessed, is not attended to, but **(b)** its impressions are overpowered by the stronger impressions of the ordinary senses.

" We easily conceive that . . . **(c)** our new force or influence may, like light, traverse the universe without difficulty, while, like heat, it may be able to penetrate through all objects, even through walls of brick or stone. And such precisely is the character of Baron von Reichenbach's **odyle** [Gr.: *h-od-os*, way, movement; *h-yle*, matter], save that it moved with less velocity than light and passed through solid bodies much more easily than heat."

" I may point to the very frequent, in some cases universal, occurrence of luminous emanations from all objects thus seen by the sleeper, nay, often seen by him while awake (as in the case of the light from the tips of the fingers of the operator or of other parties present),

" first, as indicating that an emanation of some kind . . . really does proceed from bodies in general, and

" secondly, as confirming the results of the researches of Baron von Reichenbach, who has proved . . . the existence of a peculiar influence (force, fluid, or imponderable agent) in all forms of matter and pervading the universe, the action of which is perceived in various forms by a large proportion of mankind, and always very distinctly by spontaneous somnambulists. **It is in this direction that we shall most probably find the explanation so eagerly sought after."**

Gregory wrote the foregoing for the first edition of his book in 1851. But in the *British Spiritual Telegraph* of 23rd August, 1857, a penny weekly spiritualistic newspaper published in Keighley, Yorkshire, a letter appears from him, written just seven months before his death, in which he states his opinion " that there is a great analogy between certain spiritual communications, or other facts, and the phenomena of clairvoyance. . . . My sole object," he continues, " is to ascertain the truth. My feelings are entirely in favour of Spiritualism, but I cannot feel thoroughly and logically satisfied until facts and arguments are produced *which render every other theory untenable.* . . . The hypothesis of disembodied spirits as the cause of the phenomena [*i.e. the phenomena of spiritual communications, not the phenomena of clairvoyance*] is by far the simplest and the best."

A sensitive, we must note, is not always a clairvoyant. Some undoubted sensitives go through a whole lifetime without exercising a single clairvoyant or clairaudient act. Many, again, only exercise such acts fitfully, and often find themselves bereft of the desired power when they most of all wish to exercise it. What the conditions are which determine their power to use their constitutional clairvoyant or clairaudient faculty they themselves do not know. Nor apparently, so far at any rate, does anyone else. To acquire reliable information on the point is the task now before us. Gregory writes (*Anim. Mag.*, p. 5): " The sleeper in the mesmeric state has a consciousness quite separate and distinct from his ordinary consciousness. He is in fact, if not a different individual, yet the same individual in a different and distinct phase of his being, and that phase a higher one. . . . His whole manner seems to undergo a refinement. . . . It would seem as if the brute or animal propensities were laid to rest, while the intellect and higher sentiments shone forth." And it seems reasonable to draw the same distinction between the sensitive in power and the sensitive in act even when he is awake—always of course bearing " relativity " in mind. Sleeping and waking are but relative terms. Some people, we say, seem never properly awake their whole lives through. Otherwise, why should King Gautama of Nepaul have called himself the Buddha, i.e. the Awakened ?

Sir Oliver J. Lodge : *Raymond Revised*, 1922 (p. 220), writes : " I am as convinced of existence on the other side of death as I am of existence here. It may be said, you cannot be as sure as you are of sensory experience. I say I can. A physicist is never limited to direct sensory impressions : he has to deal with a multitude of conceptions and things for which he has no physical organ. The dynamical theory of heat, for instance, and of gases, the theories of electricity, of magnetism, of chemical affinity, of cohesion, aye, and his apprehension of the Ether itself, lead him into regions where sight and hearing and touch are impotent as direct witnesses, where they are no longer efficient guides."

For Mr. (later Sir) William Crookes's experiments —unaccountable movements of balanced board recorded by weighing machine, and playing of scientifically isolated concertina—with Mr. Daniel Dunglas Home as medium or high-sensitive in the year 1870, in the presence of (1) Dr. Huggins, Vice-President of the Royal Society, (2) Serjeant Cox, (3) Mr. William Crookes's brother, and (4) Mr. William Crookes's chemical assistant, brought forward as proving

> Reichenbach's " odic molecular movement "
> *utilized by an unseen, unknown, intelligent operator,*

see *Quarterly Journal of Science*, vol. vii., p. 316, July 1870 ; see also pamphlet of 15 pages entitled *Psychic Power—Spirit Power : Experimental Investigations of W. Crookes, Dr. Huggins, Serjeant Cox, and Lord Lindsay*, 2nd thousand, reprinted from *The Spiritualist* newspaper, published by E. W. Allen, Ave Maria Lane, E.C., 1871. This pamphlet includes a letter from Lord Lindsay (later Earl of Crawford, compiler and editor of the learned *Bibliotheca Lindesiana*), dated 14th July, 1871, and detailing

> D. D. Home's visualization of *light from a magnet, as per Reichenbach,* and a levitation of Home's own body in and out of windows.

A passage tending to show the necessity of guidance from Reichenbach's investigations occurs from Crookes's pen in the above pamphlet, p. 3, where, speaking of D. D. Home, he says :

" These experiments appear conclusively to establish the existence of a new force, in some unknown manner connected with the human organization, which for convenience may be called the Psychic Force. . . . It is mainly owing to the many opportunities I have had of carrying on my investigation in his presence that I am enabled to confirm so conclusively the existence of this force. The experiments I have tried have been very numerous, but owing to our

(1) *imperfect knowledge of the conditions which favour or oppose manifestations of this force,* to the

(2) *apparently capricious manner in which it is exerted,* and to the fact that Mr. Home himself is subject to

(3) *unaccountable ebbs and flows of force,*

it has but seldom happened that a result obtained on one occasion should be subsequently confirmed and tested with apparatus specially contrived for the purpose."

The necessity of continued methodic investigation —and that on the solid foundations of nature laid bare by Reichenbach—is in fact obvious. If a natural force exists, it is constant *per se* and *in se* : it is only our scientific enthusiasm which is inconstant.

SUPPLEMENT II

DIFFERENCES BETWEEN OD AND HEAT, ELECTRICITY, AND MAGNETISM RESPECTIVELY

"UNDER the term odyle," writes Reichenbach *Researches (ed. Greg.*, p. 242), " I collect and unite all the physical phenomena occurring in the course of these researches, which cannot be brought under any of the hitherto admitted imponderables, and also the **vis occulta** which produces them. It remains for future investigation to determine whether and to what extent these phenomena will admit of being distributed among, or transferred to, the known forces above mentioned." But, in any event, he adds, " we shall never be able to do without the word odyle, or some equivalent term, on the adoption of which men may agree. Such a term must always be required to embrace a mass of phenomena, which cannot with propriety or accuracy be registered save as a peculiar group."

Meantime he sets down, and adheres firmly to, the following

DIFFERENCES :

[Ibid., pp. 230 sqq.]

A. BETWEEN ODYLE AND HEAT

a. Od affects neither thermometer nor thermoscope.

b (a). A right hand cools sensitives, warms thermoscope.

(β) A sunbeam cools sensitives, warms meter.

(γ) Moonlight warms sensitives, has no effect on thermoscope.

(δ) Fire radiates cold to sensitives, heat to the thermometer.

(ε) Chemical processes cool sensitives, often indicate disengagement of heat on thermoscope.

c. Od far more conductible through metals than heat. Copper wire will only conduct heat through a few inches, but od through 70 feet or more.

d. Od passes very easily through thick bodies, e.g. walls, impervious to solar heat : sensitives inside a house instantly distinguish a sun-rayed outside wall (by its sensation of cool) from a shaded one.

e. Od from magnets, crystals, hands, or trees, felt through air at 400 feet distance : no calorific radiations from bodies in the ordinary temperature indicated by any instrument at such distance.

f. Odylic heat and cold does not affect density or volume of bodies.

g. High sensitives perceive very great differences of apparent temperature between different colours of solar, lunar, and combustion spectrum.

h. Wires appear glowing hot to the sensitive, which are not so to ordinary sense and thermoscope.

i. Sun-rayed water is cooler to the sensitive than shaded water.

k. A porcelain or wooden rod heated at one end grows very cold to the sensitive holding the other end.

l. Heat itself under certain circumstances produces odylic cold.

"*Therefore Heat must be essentially distinct from Odyle.*"

B. Between Odyle and Electricity

Odylic phenomena occur where electrical phenomena do not appear or, as far as we know, exist, e.g. in

1. Sunshine.
2. Moonlight.
3. The spectra of different kinds of light after transmission through glass.
4. Crystals.
5. The human hand.
6. Chemical process (in part).

a. Odyle enters into the mass of any body it charges ; free electricity stratifies itself only on the surface. Odylized water remains so after pouring from glass to glass.

Odyle may for a time charge the air in a room, whereas Faraday could not collect electricity in a room prepared for the purpose. It escaped instantly by the surface of the walls, etc.

b. Free odyle charging a body takes a quarter of an hour to several hours before dissipation by contact with other bodies : free electricity is removed by contact instantaneously.

c. Odyle—not so electricity—can be condensed in unisolated bodies.

d. (1). All bodies continuous in structure (except loosely structured linens, cottons, etc.) are equally good conductors of odyle : electricity only well conducted by metals.

(2) Odylic conduction slow—20–40 seconds in traversing 50–60 yards of wire : electricity flashes through distances a million times greater in an interval too short to be measured.

e. All bodies permeable to odyle : many bodies practically impermeable to electricity.

f. As to *actio in distans*, electricity can induce odyle at a distance at which it is powerless to induce electricity; e.g. an electrical conductor so feebly charged as only to yield a 2-inch spark excites a vivid current of odyle in a wire 6½ feet off.

g. Induction of odyle by electricity takes time— 30 seconds and upwards—to become manifest, whereas induction of electricity is instantaneous. In Schweigger's multiplicator the odylic light does not become visible till 10–15 seconds after the deflection has taken place.

h. *Duration* of odylic incomparably greater than that of electrical phenomena. A wire glowing odylically by electricity continues to glow 30–60 seconds after being taken out of the current, or for 2 minutes after the charge of a powerful Leyden jar, when it fades *slowly* out.

i. In cases, odylic light disappears sooner than the excited electricity. Electrical excitement may remain in the resin cake of an electrophore for days or weeks, whereas the odylic light slowly excited by the strokes of the fur is lost in a few minutes.

k. Many odylic flames exhibit a constant upward tendency, rising vertically ; electricity, whether in motion or at rest, exhibits no such tendency.

l. Odylo-luminous phenomena of great extent appearing over metal plates (electrified or un-isolated) do not adhere to the metallic surface, as the electrical currents do, but flow over it as the aurora borealis does over the earth.

m. (1). Odylic currents do not flow merely from the points but also from the sides of bodies, even of jagged bodies, e.g. large crystals : electricity prefers a point for exit.

(2). In a voltaic pile all the elements give out odyle, whereas only *internal* activity of the electric current and entire limitation of the current to itself is observable when the circuit is closed.

n. Odylic currents excited by electricity show great independence of their cause.

o. A positive meeting a negative odylic flame will not unite with or neutralize it ; if they cross, each carries the other with it ; if directly opposed, they mutually repel each other. Opposite electricities instantly neutralize each other with a powerful mutual attraction.

p. "An electrical specimen of shorl, like every crystal, shows at its pole a lively action on sensitives, but when warmed no change takes place ; it becomes no stronger, and the electricity thus excited is not sensibly perceived."

q. Electricity has no greater effect on sensitives than on ordinary persons—in strong contrast with the violent action of odyle on their irritable nerve.

" All this shows how great a gulf separates Odyle from Electricity."

C. Between Odyle and Magnetism

Od is produced and manifested in a multitude of cases (e.g. chemical changes, vital changes, in crystals, by friction, in spectra of solar, lunar, and candlelight, in polarized light, and in the amorphous

Mм

material world collectively), in which magnetism properly so called is not known to exist.

a. In general, od is developed alone without magnetism, magnetism never alone without od.

b. Magnetism, if any, in solar or lunar rays, so feeble that existence doubtful ; while od so powerful and varied in effect as to appear capable in certain cases " of shaking life to its very foundations."

c. Mist and cloud instantly diminishes effects of sun and moon on sensitives : " magnetism is arrested by nothing, and least of all by vapours."

d. All solids and liquids may be charged with od : only a very few bodies with magnetism, and none yet known with diamagnetism.

e. Od-charged bodies act exactly like the magnet on sensitives, but will not attract one particle of iron filings.

f. Magnetism remains in steel for years : od cannot remain in steel, iron, or water longer than about one hour : magnetism never observable in water or iron.

g. Od conducted to distance of many yards by resin, glass, wood, silk strings, cotton ribbons, etc. : magnetism never so conducted.

h. Od conducted by iron wire 50–100 feet long : latter stretched in the magnetic parallels, i.e. at right angles to meridian, and connected at one end with northward pole of nine-bar horseshoe magnet showed no trace of magnetic action at other end.

i. Sphere of radiation for od through air 160 feet and more for bodies such as hands, crystals and electrified substances: no such magnetic sphere for magnets of same size.

k. Od rays simultaneously and analogously re-fracted by prism with light rays: Haldat shows by his magnetometer or magnetoscope (*L'Institut*, 27th May, 1846, p. 647) that magnetic emanations are neither refracted nor reflected.

l. Od distributed throughout mass of body charged : magnetism, says Barlow, limited entirely to the surface.

m. Od, like electricity, surrounds itself with alternating spherical zones of opposite polarities : not so magnetism.

n. Crystals and hands of same size as magnet often surpass it in odylic power : but they will not attract even the minutest iron filings.

o. Terrestrial magnetism does not affect direction of od-charged bodies, but causes magnetic bodies to place themselves in the meridian, etc.

p. Flames of odylic poles in inorganic world (including flames from poles of horseshoe magnet) show no appreciable attraction for each other : magnetic poles and their lines of force exhibit mutually the very strongest attraction.

q. No upward tendency observed in magnetism : odylic flames from horseshoe magnet held hori-zontally flow horizontally for a space, and then both curve upwards.

r. Odylic efflux from magnet continues—though more feebly—when magnetic efflux arrested by detachment of armature.

s. Same phenomenon as (r) occurs on neutraliza-tion of opposite poles of magnets by junction.

t. " Magnets, placed in the electric atmosphere of the conductor, can be made to invert the position of the *odylic* poles [*by turning the positive, southward, red-glowing side of the magnet towards the positively charged conductor*] while that of the magnetic poles remains unchanged."

u. Magnetic effects appear and disappear *instantaneously* on start and interruption of magnetic current, while odylic effects lag behind in both cases.

v. Powerful sources of od fail to induce magnetic current in coil by induction, when a magnetic needle possessing only a hundredth of the odylic power will do so instantly.

w. A magnetic bar gaining in odic power by communication from like hand or like crystalline pole will not support one more grain of iron than before.

x. Let northward pole project from left hand and southward be held in palm, reversing action in (w), and its blue flame turns to red, while the pole itself continues unchangeably magneto-negative.

y. Odylic flame of magnet may be extinguished by approach of organized living being, without any change in the magnetic power.

z. Moon acts odylo-positively on all sensitives, while Kreil [*distinguished astronomer of Prague: in his " Astronomical and Meteorological Annual,"* p. 104] proves moon to be negative magnetically, by [*very feebly*] attracting southward pole of needle on side turned towards earth. Apparent contradiction removed on consideration of fact that it is only the *luminous* rays of the moon which entail *odylic* action on sensitives : the latter ceases, at least in great part, on exclusion of the luminous rays, while " magnetic action, which penetrates all things, could not be excluded " by their exclusion.

aa. " Of diamagnetism we know only repulsions ; which may finally, according to the observations of Haldat, admit of being referred to ordinary magnetic phenomena."

bb. But a bar of iron lying horizontally in the plane of the magnetic *meridian* is *cooler* to the sensitive at its northward end than when depressed to an angle of 65° with the horizon and thus horizontal in the plane of the magnetic *inclination*.

cc. Magnetic polarity of unevenly numbered lamellæ of compound magnet is same in all lamellæ at each end of magnet, while lamellæ are shown by colours of their glow to sensitive as alternately blue and red, blue predominating [*by number of lamellæ affected*] on northward and red on southward side.

dd. " In the limbs of a horseshoe magnet, during the process of drawing it along another magnet, in a certain limb of the compound magnet positive magnetism and negative odylo-luminous emanations occurred at the same time."

" *For the present, therefore, the identity of odyle with magnetism is entirely out of the question.*"

[The above *Differences* are condensed from Professor Wm. Gregory's English edition of Reichenbach's *Researches*.]

SUPPLEMENT III

Suggestions for Experiments to Bring the Effects of Odic Force within the Ken of Non-sensitives

REICHENBACH observes (Letter iii. p. 17) that the od reflected from the prism exposed to the sun differs polarically from the od that passes through. The reflected od is negative—cool, agreeable, blue end of solar spectrum; the refracted od is positive— lukewarm, nauseating, orange end of spectrum.

A non-professional medium and sensitive of high power and integrity informs me that on the only occasion during her lifetime when she consulted a professional crystal-gazer, she observed that the egg-shaped crystal, placed longitudinally between herself (B) and crystal-gazer (A) as A and B sat facing each other on opposite sides of the table supporting the crystal, showed pink at her end (B's), and blue at the gazer's end (A's); and that there was a very little streak cf pale gold in the centre. B received the inward impression upon her mind that it was she herself and her surroundings that dominated the crystal. She asked the crystal-gazer if she (A) saw anything of this colouration, and A replied in the negative; she added that she had never during her lifetime been aware of any such colouration being shown by her crystal. B left the sitting when it had terminated with the conviction that A was a perfectly genuine and honest medium.

As our object now is to discover a means by which the effects of odic force may be brought within the ken of the non-sensitive, just as, say, the effects of the invisible X-rays are brought within his ken, I proceed to make a brief quotation from an authoritative scientific work dealing with the phenomena of the vacuum tube :

" When a current of electricity from an induction coil or influence machine is sent between two metal electrodes fused into the ends of a glass tube (say twelve inches long) from which the air is gradually withdrawn by a pump, the tube presents a continuous succession of striking appearances.

" At high pressures air is a very bad conductor of electricity, and a large force is necessary to produce a visible discharge while the pressure remains in the region of atmospheric. But a reduction of pressure facilitates the passage of the spark, which after a time loses its noisy character and is replaced by a collection of sinuous and irregular pink streamers, which later broaden and fill almost the whole of the tube with a pink diffuse glow known as the **positive column.**

" Meanwhile the cathode—the electrode by which the current leaves the tube [*that by which it enters is the anode*]—assumes at its tip a luminous tuft—**the negative glow**—violet in colour, which later grows until it completely envelops the cathode. Between these two luminous glows comes a darker, ill-defined region called the **Faraday dark-space.**" . . . G. W. C. Kaye, Director of the National Physical Laboratory, *X-rays*, 4th ed., 1923, p. 1.

Later, " the glass walls of the tube are seen to fluoresce with an olive-green light," and, " as the exhaustion proceeds, this fluorescence disappears, the negative glow detaches itself like a shell from the cathode, while a new violet film forms and spreads over the surface of the cathode. Thus the negative glow now consists of two parts : they are separated from each other by a narrow, dark region called the **Crooke's** or **Cathode dark-space.** [*Ibid.*, p. 2.]

This authoritative statement introduces us to the rudiments of the **magnetic spectrum,** which Kaye tells us [*Ibid.*, p. 15] was first observed by Birkeland in 1896.

It gives me the occasion to argue, for the benefit of the student of Reichenbach's *Odic-Magnetic Letters* who wishes to ascertain whether or not Reichenbach deals with objective facts, as follows :

As electricity passes with practically instantaneous velocity from point to point, and as the colour-phenomena of the vacuum tube only become apparent slowly and progressively, showing their polarization with greater and greater distinctness to the eye of the ordinary non-sensitive observer as the air within the tube becomes more and more rarefied, it may fairly be argued that it is not the electricity itself, but electrified *matter* of some sort, which exhibits the polarized colour-phenomenon.

What is *this matter* ? Is it the matter of the mixed nitrogen and oxygen gases of which the air is composed ? Or is it the matter of the water vapour (H_2O) contained in the air ? Or—a third alternative —is it the matter of the od permeating the air ?

Od must be there : there cannot be a cubic foot of atmosphere on earth without the ever-present trans-verberant od, which cannot, according to Reichenbach's experiences [see especially Letter xii.], be eliminated or isolated from anything in Nature, but is being constantly radiated into the air from living organisms and, secondarily, from a large number of minerals and metals.

Or—a fourth alternative—is it the matter of the dust suspended in the air within the tube?

To proceed along the path of *prima facie* probabilities in answering these questions, I conclude, first, that the matter bearing the colour-illumination is not the dust, as that is withdrawn with the air pumped out, and the more (up to 1 mm. pressure) the air is pumped out the brighter and more definite grows the colour apparition. The same argument applies to the water vapour, a substance almost as gross as the dust. Now we are thrown back on the finer elements, the nitrogen, the oxygen, and the od.

But nitrogen and oxygen can both be liquefied as separate gases, and they can be liquefied together in their mixture as air : they are just as much grosser than od, then, as the water, which, whether running underground or still in glass tumblers, Reichenbach has shown charged with od and giving off od. At the same time he has shown, with the greatest probability, that od is itself something material [see especially Letter xvi.] It is apparently a highly subtle form of matter, constituting possibly enough the medium through which organized living matter is controlled by mind.

Now we are in search of *a material something* within the tube for the electrical force—whatever " electrical force " may be—to act upon and evince that action by a display of polarized pyrotechnics. Why should not that material something be the od within the tube?

If so, the colour-phenomenon might perhaps be more precisely and properly called an odic than an electric phenomenon. In lecturing on the aurora borealis at the Imperial College of Science and Technology on 14th January, 1925, under the presidency of Lord Rayleigh, Professor Sydney Chapman stated that " auroræ were produced by streams of electric corpuscles shot out from disturbed regions of the sun's surface—often associated with sunspots. These electric particles," he said, " were deflected by the earth's magnetic field and guided towards the northern or southern polar regions. They rushed into the earth's atmosphere with great momentum and penetrated to a distance of sixty miles above ground. On their way they broke up many molecules, tearing off electrons, and when these molecules and electrons recombined the energy given up by the incoming particles in the effort of separation was reproduced as light." (*The Times*, 15th Jan., 1925.)

The report made no mention of any proof given by Professor Chapman for his statement, and till such is amply forthcoming a fairly robust faith is required to supplement the science in the theory, especially in view of Reichenbach's less violent, if still hypothetic, explanation of the aurora borealis, in Letter xiv., as being the positive od-light generated spontaneously by the positive northern pole of the earth. It is, at all events, the less alarming theory of the two. If electric corpuscles are shot into us by the sun, a body now stated by our scientific calculators to be 20,000,000 times the size of our earth, we naturally ask our imaginations : What next? We may stand the shock of the corpuscula : but what about the corpora, when *they* begin to fly?

At any rate, if od is not to be distinguished from electricity, we shall, in view of the evidence so carefully gathered by Reichenbach as to the manifold odic functions of the living human body, have to build up a very large science of " Human Electricity " to replace that of the odic force as the medium between the human principle of vitality and the human nerve, between the human will and the human act, between the human intelligence and the disposition of the pictures of the material imagination which enable the intelligence of one man to communicate his thoughts and convictions to the intelligence of his fellow-man. Is electricity able to do all that ? Od may be. It claims to be the finest form of matter yet known to the human mind, and the only form fine enough to be directly tractable by the human will. And, moreover, it reads like a homely, tractable, quiet kind of force, one well adapted to rein in and urge along the human body in obedience to the dictates of the human spirit (by which I mean the compost of intelligence and will of which our own veriest, inmost self is made), and not a wild, fiery Pegasus like electricity, as likely to prostrate us any moment by a kick as to elevate our thoughts into the regions we desire.

Will a science of human electricity be any bit more profitable than a science of animal magnetism? Probably not one whit.

If the conjecture that the colour-phenomena within the Crookes's vacuum tube are odic (a) *rather than* electric, or (b) *as well as* electric, be found to lie in the direction of the truth, then we may perhaps be well on the way to bring the effects of odic force within the domain of the ordinary non-sensitive's sensorium. Might I suggest how, in addition to a reconstitution of the experiments described by Reichenbach, the test of further scientific experimentation might be applied to what we already know, or assume, in furtherance of this desired end?

I suggest as follows :

1. Reichenbach, so far as I know, never experimented systematically with his foci of odic force *in vacuo*. Perhaps (*a*) a crystal placed in a Crookes's tube, and workable on a pivot, so as to test polarity by variations of axis, would, without any electric current being passed through the tube, display on the creation of the vacuum a phenomenon of polarized light perceptible by the ordinary non-sensitive person. Or (*b*), if not perceptible by him in the daylight, it might become perceptible to him in the dark. We must not forget the relativity of such terms and conditions as darkness and light.

As a special incitement towards making this experiment, I should like to draw attention to a particular point of resemblance between the glow of a cathode in the X-ray tube and the phenomenon of the human aura. On looking at the cathode, ordinary non-sensitives can distinguish a sort of colourless neutral zone between the cathode and the violet glow known as the Crookes dark-space, and, similarly, sensitives, on looking at the odic emanation from the fingers against a dark background, note a dark space immediately surrounding each fingertip, and, for the matter of that, each finger throughout its entire length. Each finger in this way seems *framed* with light, a dark margin or mounting existing between the finger and the frame. The same is observable with other parts of the body, and, presumably, all over the human surface.

2. The experiment would have to be carried out also with **all** the odic foci verified by Reichenbach, including the introduction into the vacuum tube of a healthily aura-diffusing human hand, closed round at the wrist with a soft rubber fitting to exclude the

air. Would the vacuum make the aura visible to non-sensitives? If not, then would it make the aura invisible to sensitives? Or how would it affect it in the sensitives' view? Would it decrease visibility, or increase it? Much might be learnt. First left hand, then right, then both together would have to be tried.

3. Again, Kaye points out in his book, *X-rays* (4th ed., 1923, p. 5), that when a tiny paddle-wheel of mica is placed within the vacuum-tube the rays proceeding from the cathode have been sufficient to make it revolve, but that it has been proved that the rays in question were *not electrical* rays, but *heat* rays. Now Reichenbach states (*Aphorisms*, pp. 64–71) that a card may be turned by the odic current from a **high**-sensitive's finger-tips, and that the photographic effects of odic rays, contrary to those of the equally invisible X-rays, are arrested by the thinnest plate of glass, while their vision-exciting effects pass through. It may thus be possible that the chemically working rays of od, plus perhaps other descriptions of odic rays in the bundle, proceeding from a cold crystal or other odic focus in a cold vacuum-tube, would impinge upon the blades of a very delicate paddle-wheel *in vacuo*, and might possibly be brought to turn it. If so, then od-rays are subject to filtration just as X-rays are, and might perhaps be similarly segregated from the therapeutic point of view into penetrating, beneficent, short-wave, homogeneous od-rays, and non-penetrative, dermatitic, long-wave, heterogeneous od-rays. It would be worth while testing the matter by experiment, especially in view of the undoubtedly proved beneficent effect of certain passes of the gifted and well-informed therapeutic operator's hands, dealt with by Reichenbach in Letter vii. and elsewhere.

4. The photographic experiments in progress at the British School of Psychic Science, 59 Holland Park, W.11, are stated in the *Quarterly Transactions* (April 1925) of that institute to show that the emanation from a sensitive's fingers had an actinic effect on a sensitized surface. For instance, the operator, Mr. F. W. Warrick, Fellow of the Chemical Society, reports (p. 32) :

" I next moistened a piece of white notepaper, 8in. by 5in., with starch-paste which contained 10 per cent. of potassium iodide. I placed this paper upon a piece of cardboard of the same size, and laid the whole on Mrs. Deane's left palm. She held her right hand over it at a distance of half an inch from the surface. I transcribe the following from my notes :

" In the position of the palm of her hand appeared a large S 2 in. long and $\frac{3}{8}$-in. thick, pale yellow in colour. There was also a pink streak at the side of it about $\frac{3}{4}$-in. by $\frac{1}{4}$-in., with a small yellow oval at one end of it."

Does this yellow colouration proceed from the aura mounting upwards from the sensitive's positive left hand, and penetrating to the sensitized surface, while a blue colouration would be attributable to the aura from the negative right hand ? If so, then Reichenbach's theory receives confirmation, both as to the special polaric colouration and the upward movement of the aura, and the confirmation is of a nature perceptible by the non-sensitive as well as the sensitive.

The editor of the *Transactions* adds in a note, to explain the S form of the marking referred to in the quoted passage : " A Deane control has stated recently that the S represents the initial of the 'operator,' a deceased scientist." This statement I leave undiscussed.

A note as to the N-rays, stated to have been isolated in 1905 in the vacuum-tube by Professor R. Blondlot, of the University of Nancy, France, seems to be here in place. In his short booklet, *N-rays*, translated by J. Garcin, the professor writes to the effect that his experimentation " reveals a new species of radiations emitted by the focus-tube, which traverse aluminium, black paper, wood, etc. [*as od-rays do*]. These are plane-polarized from the moment of their emission, are susceptible of rotatory and elliptic polarization, are refracted, reflected, diffused, but *produce neither fluoresence nor photographic action.*" They can consequently be identical neither with X-rays nor odic rays, both of which have photographic action.

The statement was made recently by Sir Arthur Conan Doyle in Paris, at the Congress of the International Spiritualists' Federation, that spiritualism is " a philosophy and a religion." If that be all that there is to be said in the matter, the interest of the scientist and the enlightened public will scarcely be aroused. The world is surfeited with philosophies and religions. But if it can be shown that sensitivity in various degrees to an odic force in operation is a biological fact, then the phenomenon of " spirit intercourse," with all that it implies, will at once become a matter of absorbing interest to the entire human race.

F. D. O'BYRNE.

London, 13th September, 1925.

Triumph of the Human Spirit: The Greatest Achievements of the Human Soul and How Its Power Can Change Your Life, by Paul Tice.  A triumph of the human spirit happens when we know we are right about something, put our heart into achieving its goal, and then succeed. There is no better feeling. People throughout history have triumphed while fighting for the highest ideal of all -- spiritual truth. Tice brings you back to relive and explore history's most incredible spiritual moments, bringing you into the lives of visionaries and great leaders who were in touch with their souls and followed their hearts. They explored God in their own way, exposed corruption and false teachings, or freed themselves and others from suppression. People like Gandhi, Joan of Arc, and Dr. King expressed exactly what they believed and changed the entire course of history. They were eliminated through violence, but on a spiritual level achieved victory because of their strong moral cause. Their spirit lives on, and the world was greatly improved. Tice covers other movements and people who may have physically failed, but spiritually triumphed. This book not only documents the history of spiritual giants, it shows how you can achieve your own spiritual triumph. In today's world we are free to explore the truth without fear of being tortured or executed. As a result, the rewards are great. Various exercises will strengthen the soul and reveal its hidden power. One can discover their true spiritual source with this work and will be able to tap into it. This is the perfect book for all those who believe in spiritual freedom and have a passion for the truth. **ISBN 1-885395-57-4 · 295 pages · 6 x 9 · trade paper · illustrated · $19.95**

Mysteries Explored: The Search for Human Origins, UFOs, and Religious Beginnings, by Jack Barranger and Paul Tice. Jack Barranger and Paul Tice are two authors who have combined forces in an overall investigation into human origins, religion, mythology, UFOs, and other unexplained phenomena. In the first chapter, "The Legacy of Zecharia Sitchin", Barranger covers the importance of Sitchin's *Earth Chronicles* books, which is creating a revolution in the way we look at our past. In "The First Dragon" chapter, Tice examines the earliest known story containing dragons, coming from Sumerian/Babylonian mythology. In "Past Shock", Barranger suggests that events which happened thousands of years ago very strongly impact humanity today. In "UFOs: From Earth or Outer Space?" Tice explores the evidence for aliens being from other earthly dimensions as opposed to having an extraterrestrial origin. "Is Religion Harmful?" looks at the origins of religion and why the entire idea may no longer be working for us, while "A Call to Heresy" shows how Jesus and the Buddha were considered heretics in their day, and how we have reached a critical point in our present spiritual development that requires another such leap. Aside from these chapters, the book also contains a number of outrageous (but discontinued) newsletters, including: Promethean Fire, Pleiadian Poop, and Intrusions. **ISBN 1-58509-101-4 · 104 pages · 6 x 9 · trade paper · $12.95**

Mushrooms and Mankind: The Impact of Mushrooms on Human Consciousness and Religion, by James Arthur.  For thousands of years on our planet, humanity has been involved in a symbiotic relationship with plants. Not only have plants supplied mankind with a never-ending food source, the necessary nourishment for our bodies and life itself, but they have also served us in another way: an extremely important and intricate one, yet an often overlooked one. This book uncovers the natural link between man, consciousness, and God. This discovery may at first seem abstract, wishful thinking, or even impossible; yet as evidence presented on these pages unfolds, you may find that its understanding does not require as much of a leap of faith as you might think. This may be the most significant discovery in the entire field of religious knowledge ever to happen in the history of mankind. Should people use this knowledge, it will allow many on this planet to put their differences aside, and join in the understanding that each and every one of us may now experience that which has been, until this time, hidden away in the recesses of our spiritual history. We may at last be able to open ourselves to an entirely new and valuable consciousness. **ISBN 1-58509-151-0 · 180 pages · 6 x 9 · trade paper · $16.95**

Vril or Vital Magnetism, **with an introduction by Paul Tice.** Vril is another name for the life energy of the body, known in other cultures worldwide as mana, prana, chi, or vital force. Most of the ancient cultures of the world were aware of this important force and worked to make use of it. In today's world, especially in the West, we move along through life completely oblivious to this truly vital energy. Although this force cannot be seen, it is the life force within our bodies. It takes energy from food and provides muscles with energy, which in turn allows us to move about in daily life as well as grow and metabolize. Nourishment, digestion, and elimination are all driven by the life force. Vril also has a connection to the mind, and methods can be employed to store up its energy and use it constructively. Vril is not manufactured in the human body, but can be collected and used effectively. This energy

is present in water, and especially in the air. This is why breathing is so important in the practice of meditation. A deeper part of us comes alive while we meditate, due to increased vital energy in the body combined with the relaxation of the mind. This book is by far the best guidebook known to this mysterious and powerful force. The exact mechanics of how it works are detailed, plus methods of gathering, conserving, and using its power. The exercises given are powerful and they work. This is really more of a self-help book than a simple fact book or mystical overview. **ISBN 1-58509-030-1 • 124 pages • 5 1/2 x 8 1/2 • trade paper • $12.95**

The New Revelation: The Coming of a New Spiritual Paradigm, **by Arthur Conan Doyle.** Arthur Conan Doyle was a famous mystery writer (*The Adventures of Sherlock Holmes*) and spiritualist from the early twentieth century who predicted, with this book, the coming of a spiritually based religion in the future. This "New Revelation" seems to have taken shape. as he had predicted, in the form of the New Age Movement. Doyle based this book on the spiritualist movement of his day which included channeling, seances, automatic writing, and a variety of other strange, psychic occurrences. He investigated these things thoroughly and came away convinced that more proof existed within these realms than could be found within any standard religion. He acknowledged some of the fraudulent scams that were exposed in spiritual circles and stated that serious researchers

like himself completely deplored such events and that they were not representative of the larger areas of authentic psychic phenomena. As our more modern research continues, we may be able to clear up some of the deeper mysteries concerning who we are and where we go after death. If this should happen it would truly qualify as a "new revelation", one that would shake our religious foundations to the core. The "Old Revelation", Doyle says, has lost its power through bigotry, mismanagement, materialism, and claims of infallibility that no longer hold up. A new world of personal discovery awaits us, as an alternative, and one can begin to explore it now by reading this classic work. **ISBN 1-58509-220-7 • 124 pages • 6 x 9 • trade paper • $12.95**

Reason and Belief: The Impact of Scientific Discovery on Religious and Spiritual Faith, **by Sir Oliver Lodge.** Sir Oliver Lodge was a respected writer from the early twentieth century. At this time, there were a number of scientific advances that caused one to consider the ramifications of these new discoveries on the religious and spiritual beliefs of the day. But the impact of science may not be so great on spiritual matters in the final analysis, according to Lodge. He puts forth a number of interesting examples. He does not champion science as the final answer, which is what makes this book so interesting. Science is still helpful. It is a tool that is allowing us to reach spiritual answers that have so far not been found. Lodge actively searches for spiritual answers with great wisdom throughout the book and, when necessary, backs off from his great spiritual knowledge and explores our grasp of science to help us along. The last third of the book covers the scope of science. Lodge is a mystic who states that science is useful, but will never embrace the whole of knowledge. Thinking that science is and will be the final answer is the mistake in thinking that scientists of today fall into. Scientists depend solely on a limited bandwidth of discipline that sometimes creates blinders, as found on a racehorse that can only run in a straight line. Lodge takes the blinders off, and opens us up to the larger possibilities around us. **ISBN 1-58509-226-6 • 180 pages • 6 x 9 • trade paper • $17.95**

Of Heaven and Earth: Essays Presented at the First Sitchin Studies Day, edited by Zecharia Sitchin. ISBN 1-885395-17-5 • 164 pages • 5 1/2 x 8 1/2 • trade paper • illustrated • $14.95

God Games: What Do You Do Forever?, by Neil Freer. ISBN 1-885395-39-6 • 312 pages • 6 x 9 • trade paper • $19.95

Space Travelers and the Genesis of the Human Form: Evidence of Intelligent Contact in the Solar System, by Joan d'Arc. ISBN 1-58509-127-8 • 208 pages • 6 x 9 • trade paper • illustrated • $18.95

Humanity's Extraterrestrial Origins: ET Influences on Humankind's Biological and Cultural Evolution, by Dr. Arthur David Horn with Lynette Mallory-Horn. ISBN 3-931652-31-9 • 373 pages • 6 x 9 • trade paper • $17.00

Past Shock: The Origin of Religion and Its Impact on the Human Soul, by Jack Barranger. ISBN 1-885395-08-6 • 126 pages • 6 x 9 • trade paper • illustrated • $12.95

Flying Serpents and Dragons: The Story of Mankind's Reptilian Past, by R.A. Boulay. ISBN 1-885395-38-8 • 276 pages • 6 x 9 • trade paper • illustrated • $19.95

Triumph of the Human Spirit: The Greatest Achievements of the Human Soul and How Its Power Can Change Your Life, by Paul Tice. ISBN 1-885395-57-4 • 295 pages • 6 x 9 • trade paper • illustrated • $19.95

Mysteries Explored: The Search for Human Origins, UFOs, and Religious Beginnings, by Jack Barranger and Paul Tice. ISBN 1-58509-101-4 • 104 pages • 6 x 9 • trade paper • $12.95

Mushrooms and Mankind: The Impact of Mushrooms on Human Consciousness and Religion, by James Arthur. ISBN 1-58509-151-0 • 180 pages • 6 x 9 • trade paper • $16.95

Vril or Vital Magnetism, with an Introduction by Paul Tice. ISBN 1-58509-030-1 • 124 pages • 5 1/2 x 8 1/2 • trade paper • $12.95

The Odic Force: Letters on Od and Magnetism, by Karl von Reichenbach. ISBN 1-58509-001-8 • 192 pages • 6 x 9 • trade paper • $15.95

The New Revelation: The Coming of a New Spiritual Paradigm, by Arthur Conan Doyle. ISBN 1-58509-220-7 • 124 pages • 6 x 9 • trade paper • $12.95

The Astral World: Its Scenes, Dwellers, and Phenomena, by Swami Panchadasi. ISBN 1-58509-071-9 • 104 pages • 6 x 9 • trade paper • $11.95

Reason and Belief: The Impact of Scientific Discovery on Religious and Spiritual Faith, by Sir Oliver Lodge. ISBN 1-58509-226-6 • 180 pages • 6 x 9 • trade paper • $17.95

William Blake: A Biography, by Basil De Selincourt. ISBN 1-58509-225-8 • 384 pages • 6 x 9 • trade paper • $28.95

The Divine Pymander: And Other Writings of Hermes Trismegistus, translated by John D. Chambers. ISBN 1-58509-046-8 • 196 pages • 6 x 9 • trade paper • $16.95

Theosophy and The Secret Doctrine, by Harriet L. Henderson. Includes *H.P. Blavatsky: An Outline of Her Life*, by Herbert Whyte, ISBN 1-58509-075-1 • 132 pages • 6 x 9 • trade paper • $13.95

The Light of Egypt, Volume One: The Science of the Soul and the Stars, by Thomas H. Burgoyne. ISBN 1-58509-051-4 • 320 pages • 6 x 9 • trade paper • illustrated • $24.95

The Light of Egypt, Volume Two: The Science of the Soul and the Stars, by Thomas H. Burgoyne. ISBN 1-58509-052-2 • 224 pages • 6 x 9 • trade paper • illustrated • $17.95

The Jumping Frog and 18 Other Stories: 19 Unforgettable Mark Twain Stories, by Mark Twain. ISBN 1-58509-200-2 • 128 pages • 6 x 9 • trade paper • $12.95

The Devil's Dictionary: A Guidebook for Cynics, by Ambrose Bierce. ISBN 1-58509-016-6 • 144 pages • 6 x 9 • trade paper • $12.95

The Smoky God: Or The Voyage to the Inner World, by Willis George Emerson. ISBN 1-58509-067-0 • 184 pages • 6 x 9 • trade paper • illustrated • $15.95

A Short History of the World, by H.G. Wells. ISBN 1-58509-211-8 • 320 pages • 6 x 9 • trade paper • $24.95

The Voyages and Discoveries of the Companions of Columbus, by Washington Irving. ISBN 1-58509-500-1 • 352 pages • 6 x 9 • hard cover • $39.95

History of Baalbek, by Michel Alouf. ISBN 1-58509-063-8 • 196 pages • 5 x 8 • trade paper • illustrated • $15.95

Ancient Egyptian Masonry: The Building Craft, by Sommers Clarke and R. Engelback. ISBN 1-58509-059-X • 350 pages • 6 x 9 • trade paper • illustrated • $26.95

That Old Time Religion: The Story of Religious Foundations, by Jordan Maxwell and Paul Tice. ISBN 1-58509-100-6 • 220 pages • 6 x 9 • trade paper • $19.95

Jumpin' Jehovah: Exposing the Atrocities of the Old Testament God, by Paul Tice. ISBN 1-58509-102-2 • 104 pages • 6 x 9 • trade paper • $12.95

The Book of Enoch: A Work of Visionary Revelation and Prophecy, Revealing Divine Secrets and Fantastic Information about Creation, Salvation, Heaven and Hell, translated by R. H. Charles. ISBN 1-58509-019-0 • 152 pages • 5 1/2 x 8 1/2 • trade paper • $13.95

The Book of Enoch: Translated from the Editor's Ethiopic Text and Edited with an Enlarged Introduction, Notes and Indexes, Together with a Reprint of the Greek Fragments, edited by R. H. Charles. ISBN 1-58509-080-8 • 448 pages • 6 x 9 • trade paper • $34.95

The Book of the Secrets of Enoch, translated from the Slavonic by W. R. Morfill. Edited, with Introduction and Notes by R. H. Charles. ISBN 1-58509-020-4 • 148 pages • 5 1/2 x 8 1/2 • trade paper • $13.95

Enuma Elish: The Seven Tablets of Creation, Volume One, by L. W. King. ISBN 1-58509-041-7 • 236 pages • 6 x 9 • trade paper • illustrated • $18.95

Enuma Elish: The Seven Tablets of Creation, Volume Two, by L. W. King. ISBN 1-58509-042-5 • 260 pages • 6 x 9 • trade paper • illustrated • $19.95

Enuma Elish, Volumes One and Two: The Seven Tablets of Creation, by L. W. King. Two volumes from above bound as one. ISBN 1-58509-043-3 • 496 pages • 6 x 9 • trade paper • illustrated • $38.90

The Archko Volume: Documents that Claim Proof to the Life, Death, and Resurrection of Christ, by Drs. McIntosh and Twyman. ISBN 1-58509-082-4 • 248 pages • 6 x 9 • trade paper • $20.95

The Lost Language of Symbolism: An Inquiry into the Origin of Certain Letters, Words, Names, Fairy-Tales, Folklore, and Mythologies, by Harold Bayley. ISBN 1-58509-070-0 • 384 pages • 6 x 9 • trade paper • $27.95

The Book of Jasher: A Suppressed Book that was Removed from the Bible, Referred to in Joshua and Second Samuel, translated by Albinus Alcuin (800 AD). ISBN 1-58509-081-6 • 304 pages • 6 x 9 • trade paper • $24.95

The Bible's Most Embarrassing Moments, with an Introduction by Paul Tice. ISBN 1-58509-025-5 • 172 pages • 5 x 8 • trade paper • $14.95

History of the Cross: The Pagan Origin and Idolatrous Adoption and Worship of the Image, by Henry Dana Ward. ISBN 1-58509-056-5 • 104 pages • 6 x 9 • trade paper • illustrated • $11.95

Was Jesus Influenced by Buddhism? A Comparative Study of the Lives and Thoughts of Gautama and Jesus, by Dwight Goddard. ISBN 1-58509-027-1 • 252 pages • 6 x 9 • trade paper • $19.95

History of the Christian Religion to the Year Two Hundred, by Charles B. Waite. ISBN 1-885395-15-9 • 556 pages • 6 x 9 • hard cover • $25.00

Symbols, Sex, and the Stars, by Ernest Busenbark. ISBN 1-885395-19-1 • 396 pages • 5 1/2 x 8 1/2 • trade paper • $22.95

History of the First Council of Nice: A World's Christian Convention, A.D. 325, by Dean Dudley. ISBN 1-58509-023-9 • 132 pages • 5 1/2 x 8 1/2 • trade paper • $12.95

The World's Sixteen Crucified Saviors, by Kersey Graves. ISBN 1-58509-018-2 • 436 pages • 5 1/2 x 8 1/2 • trade paper • $29.95

Babylonian Influence on the Bible and Popular Beliefs: A Comparative Study of Genesis I.2, by A. Smythe Palmer. ISBN 1-58509-000-X • 124 pages • 6 x 9 • trade paper • $12.95

Biography of Satan: Exposing the Origins of the Devil, by Kersey Graves. ISBN 1-885395-11-6 • 168 pages • 5 1/2 x 8 1/2 • trade paper • $13.95

The Malleus Maleficarum: The Notorious Handbook Once Used to Condemn and Punish "Witches", by Heinrich Kramer and James Sprenger. ISBN 1-58509-098-0 • 332 pages • 6 x 9 • trade paper • $25.95

Crux Ansata: An Indictment of the Roman Catholic Church, by H. G. Wells. ISBN 1-58509-210-X • 160 pages • 6 x 9 • trade paper • $14.95

Emanuel Swedenborg: The Spiritual Columbus, by U.S.E. (William Spear). ISBN 1-58509-096-4 • 208 pages • 6 x 9 • trade paper • $17.95

Dragons and Dragon Lore, by Ernest Ingersoll. ISBN 1-58509-021-2 • 228 pages • 6 x 9 • trade paper • illustrated • $17.95

The Vision of God, by Nicholas of Cusa. ISBN 1-58509-004-2 • 160 pages • 5 x 8 • trade paper • $13.95

The Historical Jesus and the Mythical Christ: Separating Fact From Fiction, by Gerald Massey. ISBN 1-58509-073-5 • 244 pages • 6 x 9 • trade paper • $18.95

Gog and Magog: The Giants in Guildhall; Their Real and Legendary History, with an Account of Other Giants at Home and Abroad, by F.W. Fairholt. ISBN 1-58509-084-0 • 172 pages • 6 x 9 • trade paper • $16.95

The Origin and Evolution of Religion, by Albert Churchward. ISBN 1-58509-078-6 • 504 pages • 6 x 9 • trade paper • $39.95

The Origin of Biblical Traditions, by Albert T. Clay. ISBN 1-58509-065-4 • 220 pages • 5 1/2 x 8 1/2 • trade paper • $17.95

Aryan Sun Myths, by Sarah Elizabeth Titcomb, Introduction by Charles Morris. ISBN 1-58509-069-7 • 192 pages • 6 x 9 • trade paper • $15.95

The Social Record of Christianity, by Joseph McCabe. Includes **The Lies and Fallacies of the Encyclopedia Britannica,** ISBN 1-58509-215-0 • 204 pages • 6 x 9 • trade paper • $17.95

The History of the Christian Religion and Church During the First Three Centuries, by Dr. Augustus Neander. ISBN 1-58509-077-8 • 112 pages • 6 x 9 • trade paper • $12.95

Ancient Symbol Worship: Influence of the Phallic Idea in the Religions of Antiquity, by Hodder M. Westropp and C. Staniland Wake. ISBN 1-58509-048-4 • 120 pages • 6 x 9 • trade paper • illustrated • $12.95

The Gnosis: Or Ancient Wisdom in the Christian Scriptures, by William Kingsland. ISBN 1-58509-047-6 • 232 pages • 6 x 9 • trade paper • $18.95

The Evolution of the Idea of God: An Inquiry into the Origin of Religions, by Grant Allen. ISBN 1-58509-074-3 • 160 pages • 6 x 9 • trade paper • $14.95

Sun Lore of All Ages: A Survey of Solar Mythology, Folklore, Customs, Worship, Festivals, and Superstition, by William Tyler Olcott. ISBN 1-58509-044-1 • 316 pages • 6 x 9 • trade paper • $24.95

Nature Worship: An Account of Phallic Faiths and Practices Ancient and Modern, by the Author of Phallicism with an Introduction by Tedd St. Rain. ISBN 1-58509-049-2 • 112 pages • 6 x 9 • trade paper • illustrated • $12.95

Life and Religion, by Max Muller. ISBN 1-885395-10-8 • 237 pages • 5 1/2 x 8 1/2 • trade paper • $14.95

Jesus: God, Man, or Myth? An Examination of the Evidence, by Herbert Cutner. ISBN 1-58509-072-7 • 304 pages • 6 x 9 • trade paper • $23.95

Pagan and Christian Creeds: Their Origin and Meaning, by Edward Carpenter. ISBN 1-58509-024-7 • 316 pages • 5 1/2 x 8 1/2 • trade paper • $24.95

The Christ Myth: A Study, by Elizabeth Evans. ISBN 1-58509-037-9 • 136 pages • 6 x 9 • trade paper • $13.95

Popery: Foe of the Church and the Republic, by Joseph F. Van Dyke. ISBN 1-58509-058-1 • 336 pages • 6 x 9 • trade paper • illustrated • $25.95

Career of Religious Ideas, by Hudson Tuttle. ISBN 1-58509-066-2 • 172 pages • 5 x 8 • trade paper • $15.95

Buddhist Suttas: Major Scriptural Writings from Early Buddhism, by T.W. Rhys Davids. ISBN 1-58509-079-4 • 376 pages • 6 x 9 • trade paper • $27.95

Early Buddhism, by T. W. Rhys Davids. Includes **Buddhist Ethics: The Way to Salvation?,** by Paul Tice. ISBN 1-58509-076-X • 112 pages • 6 x 9 • trade paper • $12.95

The Fountain-Head of Religion: A Comparative Study of the Principal Religions of the World and a Manifestation of their Common Origin from the Vedas, by Ganga Prasad. ISBN 1-58509-054-9 • 276 pages • 6 x 9 • trade paper • $22.95

India: What Can It Teach Us?, by Max Muller. ISBN 1-58509-064-6 • 284 pages • 5 1/2 x 8 1/2 • trade paper • $22.95

Matrix of Power: How the World has Been Controlled by Powerful People Without Your Knowledge, by Jordan Maxwell. ISBN 1-58509-120-0 • 104 pages • 6 x 9 • trade paper • $12.95

Cyberculture Counterconspiracy: A Steamshovel Web Reader, Volume One, edited by Kenn Thomas. ISBN 1-58509-125-1 • 180 pages • 6 x 9 • trade paper • illustrated • $16.95

Cyberculture Counterconspiracy: A Steamshovel Web Reader, Volume Two, edited by Kenn Thomas. ISBN 1-58509-126-X • 132 pages • 6 x 9 • trade paper • illustrated • $13.95

Oklahoma City Bombing: The Suppressed Truth, by Jon Rappoport. ISBN 1-885395-22-1 • 112 pages • 5 1/2 x 8 1/2 • trade paper • $12.95

The Protocols of the Learned Elders of Zion, by Victor Marsden. ISBN 1-58509-015-8 • 312 pages • 6 x 9 • trade paper • $24.95

Secret Societies and Subversive Movements, by Nesta H. Webster. ISBN 1-58509-092-1 • 432 pages • 6 x 9 • trade paper • $29.95

The Secret Doctrine of the Rosicrucians, by Magus Incognito. ISBN 1-58509-091-3 • 256 pages • 6 x 9 • trade paper • $20.95

The Origin and Evolution of Freemasonry: Connected with the Origin and Evolution of the Human Race, by Albert Churchward. ISBN 1-58509-029-8 • 240 pages • 6 x 9 • trade paper • $18.95

The Lost Key: An Explanation and Application of Masonic Symbols, by Prentiss Tucker. ISBN 1-58509-050-6 • 192 pages • 6 x 9 • trade paper • illustrated • $15.95

The Character, Claims, and Practical Workings of Freemasonry, by Rev. C.G. Finney. ISBN 1-58509-094-8 • 288 pages • 6 x 9 • trade paper • $22.95

The Secret World Government or "The Hidden Hand": The Unrevealed in History, by Maj.-Gen., Count Cherep-Spiridovich. ISBN 1-58509-093-X • 270 pages • 6 x 9 • trade paper • $21.95

The Magus, Book One: A Complete System of Occult Philosophy, by Francis Barrett. ISBN 1-58509-031-X • 200 pages • 6 x 9 • trade paper • illustrated • $16.95

The Magus, Book Two: A Complete System of Occult Philosophy, by Francis Barrett. ISBN 1-58509-032-8 • 220 pages • 6 x 9 • trade paper • illustrated • $17.95

The Magus, Book One and Two: A Complete System of Occult Philosophy, by Francis Barrett. ISBN 1-58509-033-6 • 420 pages • 6 x 9 • trade paper • illustrated • $34.90

The Key of Solomon The King, by S. Liddell MacGregor Mathers. ISBN 1-58509-022-0 • 152 pages • 6 x 9 • trade paper • illustrated • $12.95

Magic and Mystery in Tibet, by Alexandra David-Neel. ISBN 1-58509-097-2 • 352 pages • 6 x 9 • trade paper • $26.95

The Comte de St. Germain, by I. Cooper Oakley. ISBN 1-58509-068-9 • 280 pages • 6 x 9 • trade paper • illustrated • $22.95

Alchemy Rediscovered and Restored, by A. Cockren. ISBN 1-58509-028-X • 156 pages • 5 1/2 x 8 1/2 • trade paper • $13.95

The 6th and 7th Books of Moses, with an Introduction by Paul Tice. ISBN 1-58509-045-X • 188 pages • 6 x 9 • trade paper • illustrated • $16.95

Printed in the United States
220704BV00001B/22/A

9 781585 090013